The Wallace Collection
GUIDE

The Trustees of the Wallace Collection, Manchester Square,
London WIM 6BN
1992

Published with the generous assistance of
Total Oil Great Britain Ltd

COVER
Front: Watteau *Gilles and his Family* (P381) detail,
in Gallery 24
Back: Sèvres porcelain Vase and Cover (C251) detail,
in Gallery 3

TITLE PAGE
The Wallace of Craigie crest used by Sir Richard Wallace

ISBN 0 900785 39 X

Designed by Graham Johnson

Phototypeset in Monotype Baskerville Series 169
by Southern Positives and Negatives (SPAN), Lingfield, Surrey

Printed by Southwell Press

Contents

Ground floor

Women's Lavatory

Men's Lavatory

Cloakroom

Emergency Exits

Telephone

1 & Corridor	Bonington and early 19th-century paintings
2–4	French 18th-century furniture, paintings; Sèvres porcelain (Spanish and Dutch paintings in Gallery 4)
5	English paintings and French 18th-century furniture
6, 7 & Corridor	Medieval, Renaissance and Baroque works of art
8–11	Arms and armour (Orientalist paintings in Gallery 11)
12	SHOP & INFORMATION 19th-century English paintings

First floor

Introduction

The Wallace Collection was bequeathed to the nation in February 1897 by Lady Wallace. She was the widow of Sir Richard Wallace, a notable collector of works of art and also, as the illegitimate son of the 4th Marquess of Hertford, the inheritor of one of the greatest of all private collections.

By the terms of Lady Wallace's bequest the Collection is named The Wallace Collection and it remains 'unmixed with other objects of art'. Because nothing may therefore be loaned or added it enshrines an Anglo-French nineteenth-century taste. Among its many treasures are one of the finest collections of French eighteenth-century pictures, porcelain and furniture outside Paris, a remarkable display of seventeenth-century paintings and an armoury second only in England to that of the Tower of London.

The Wallace Collection is kept at Hertford House, which had been the principal London residence of the Marquesses of Hertford and was later owned by Sir Richard Wallace. It opened to the public as a national museum in June 1900.

The Founders

The 1st Marquess of Hertford

Francis Seymour-Conway (1719–94). Descended from Edward Seymour who became Lord Protector of England in 1547 and was the brother of Queen Jane Seymour. A loyal Tory courtier, he was Ambassador in Paris (1762–5), Lord Lieutenant of Ireland (1765–6) and Lord Chamberlain (1766–82). His family's property included Ragley Hall in Warwickshire (still the seat of the Marquesses of Hertford), Conway Castle in Wales, Sudbourne Hall in Suffolk and extensive estates in Ireland. He bought six of the Canalettos now in the Collection.

The 2nd Marquess of Hertford

Francis Ingram Seymour-Conway (1743–1822), son of the 1st Marquess. Like his father a loyal Tory, he was Lord of the Treasury (1774–82), Ambassador to Berlin and Vienna (1793–94) and Lord Chamberlain (1812–21). This last appointment was facilitated by his wife's protracted liaison with the Prince of Wales, later George IV.

Hertford House

7

In 1797 he acquired the lease of Manchester House (now Hertford House). He bought some notable English portraits, including Reynolds's *Nelly O'Brien*, and was given Gainsborough's *'Perdita' Robinson* by the Prince of Wales. Some pieces of Sèvres porcelain now in the Collection were also acquired by him.

The 3rd Marquess of Hertford

The 3rd Marquess of Hertford, *c*.1824 Henry Bone after Thomas Lawrence (MA3)

Francis Charles Seymour-Conway (1777–1842), son of the 2nd Marquess. He was Vice-Chamberlain in the royal household (1812–21). In 1798 he married Maria Fagnani, the illegitimate daughter of the Marchesa Fagnani. She greatly increased the family fortunes through substantial bequests from the 4th Duke of Queensberry ('Old Q') and his associate George Selwyn, who both believed that they were her father. When the 3rd Marquess and Maria visited Paris in 1802 they became estranged and thereafter led separate lives. She remained in Paris where in 1805 she bore a second son, Lord Henry Seymour (whose father was probably Count Casimir de Montrond), while the 3rd Marquess established splendid residences in London at Dorchester House (on the site of the present Dorchester Hotel) and at St Dunstan's Villa in Regent's Park (demolished in 1937). His later life was somewhat dissipated, to the extent that both Thackeray and Disraeli chose him as the model for sinister characters (Lord Steyne in *Vanity Fair* and Lord Monmouth in *Coningsby*).

The 3rd Marquess was a considerable connoisseur. He bought French furniture, gilt bronzes and Sèvres porcelain, Dutch cabinet pictures (including Netscher's *Lacemaker* and the Rembrandtesque *Good Samaritan* and *Landscape with a Coach*), as well as a few large gallery pictures, including Titian's *Perseus and Andromeda*, perhaps his most remarkable purchase. He also acted as a saleroom agent for the Prince of Wales, for whom he bought outstanding Dutch pictures which still remain in the Royal Collection. Both men were much attracted by eighteenth-century French decorative art and, like other English collectors, profited from the dissolution of many great Continental collections during the French Revolution and the Napoleonic wars.

The 4th Marquess of Hertford

The 4th Marquess of Hertford, *c*.1855

Richard Seymour-Conway (1800–70), son of the 3rd Marquess, was brought up in Paris by his mother and came to England in 1816. He was briefly an M.P. (1819–26) and a cavalry officer. He visited Constantinople in 1829, in which year he acquired a large apartment at no.2 rue Laffitte (near his mother, her second son, Lord Henry Seymour, and his own illegitimate son, Richard Jackson). By 1835, when he bought the château of Bagatelle in the Bois de Boulogne, he had determined to settle in Paris.

The 4th Marquess never married. Witty and intelligent as well as one of the richest men in Europe, he was an intimate friend of Napoleon III. But there was a neurotic side to his personality and he preferred a reclusive life. He 'would not even have drawn back his curtain to see a revolution go past in the street' wrote one contemporary, Charles Yriarte, and it was characteristic of him that he appears never to have had his portrait painted. In 1845 he visited the Irish estates from which he derived much of his income. After a stay of five weeks he went back to Paris, resolving never to return.

The last thirty years of the 4th Marquess's life were devoted to collecting works of art on a grand scale. He bought Dutch paintings (including Rembrandt's *Titus* and Hals' *The Laughing Cavalier*), many superb old masters (including masterpieces by Poussin, van Dyck, Velázquez and Rubens) and most of the nineteenth-century French and English paintings now at Hertford House. Like his father, he was attracted by the superb craftsmanship of the *ancien régime*, but he acquired a wider range of objects and on a far larger scale. He bought pictures by Watteau, Greuze, Boucher and Fragonard; many fine pieces of Sèvres porcelain, furniture by the greatest French cabinet-makers of the eighteenth century such as Gaudreaus, Cressent and Riesener, as well as miniatures, gold boxes, tapestries and sculpture. For most of his collecting life the art of the *ancien régime* had still not fully recovered from its disparagement during the French Revolution and the First Empire. In his last decade he acquired the important collection of Oriental arms and armour.

He usually bought at auction through dealers, and from the letters to his main London agent, Samuel Mawson, we know something of his motivation as a collector. His taste tended towards the pleasing and the sensuous (hence his liking for the paintings of Murillo with their 'rich, mellow quality') and he attached great importance to good condition and a known (particularly royal) provenance. He did not visit England after 1855 and he never saw some of his finest purchases, such as *The Rainbow Landscape* by Rubens, which were sent directly from the London salerooms to Hertford House.

He died at Bagatelle in August 1870 as the Prussian army advanced upon Paris, bringing the Second Empire to an end. He bequeathed his unentailed property, including his great collection, to his illegitimate son, Richard Wallace. The Marquisate was inherited by a second cousin.

Sir Richard Wallace

Sir Richard Wallace, 1888

Richard Jackson (1818–90), the illegitimate son of the 4th Marquess of Hertford and Mrs Agnes Jackson, was raised in Paris by his grandmother from the age of six. The 4th Marquess never acknowledged his paternity, and in 1842 Wallace took his mother's maiden name.

In 1870 he inherited his father's collection, the château of Bagatelle and the apartment in the rue Laffitte, the lease of Hertford House and the estates in Ireland. While Paris was besieged by the Prussians and then devastated by the uprising of the Commune, Wallace won a considerable reputation through charitable works and gifts to humanitarian causes. Among his donations were fifty drinking fountains to the city of Paris, one of which is now in the drive of Hertford House. In recognition of his philanthropy he was made a baronet in 1871, just after he had married his mistress, Julie Castelnau, the mother of his thirty-year-old son, Edmond Richard.

In 1872 he moved to London, bringing with him from Paris many of his finest works of art, probably in the belief that they would there have a safer home. While Hertford House was being converted (1872–5) to accommodate them, much of the collection was put on exhibition at the new Bethnal Green Museum where it proved a sensation, being visited by five million people.

Unlike his father, Wallace took an interest in the responsibilities that his wealth brought him, particularly in Ireland. But the circumstances of his birth and the refusal of his wife and son to become anglicized meant that he was never fully accepted within English society. After the death of his son in 1887 he returned alone to Bagatelle where he died three years later in the same room as his father.

Wallace had been secretary to the 4th Marquess and, through acting as his agent, became something of a connoisseur. He bought some superb miniatures and gold boxes, but his taste in paintings, furniture and porcelain was similar to that of his father. He showed more independence in his taste for medieval and Renaissance works of art. In 1871 he purchased the collections of European arms and armour and medieval and Renaissance decorative arts formed by the comte de Nieuwerkerke, Napoleon III's Minister of Fine Arts. In the same year he bought a selection of the arms and armour collected by Sir Samuel Meyrick and in 1872 he acquired the vicomte de Tauzia's early Italian paintings and illuminated manuscript cuttings. He bought very few works of art in the last fifteen years of his life.

Lady Wallace

Lady Wallace, c.1890

Julie-Amélie-Charlotte Castelnau (1819–97) married Richard Wallace in 1871, having been his mistress for many years. The daughter of an army officer, she is said to have been an assistant in a perfumer's shop in Paris when they first met.

In 1890 Sir Richard Wallace bequeathed to her all his property. There is no evidence that she had any enthusiasm for the great collection for which she then became responsible and, after Wallace's death, she led a secluded life at Hertford House. It was almost certainly the loyal desire to fulfil her husband's wishes that led her to leave the collection at Hertford House to the nation. Wallace himself had discussed the idea with the Treasury in the 1880s, but without success.

Sir John Murray Scott

There were still many superb pieces of eighteenth-century French furniture, sculpture and tapestry at the apartment in the rue Laffitte and at the château of Bagatelle. These, together with the properties in Suffolk and Ireland and the lease of Hertford House, Lady Wallace bequeathed to her secretary, John Murray Scott (1847–1912), who had been her principal adviser since Wallace's death. He was made a baronet in 1899.

Murray Scott sold the lease of Hertford House to the Government and became a Trustee of the Collection when it opened as a museum in 1900. During his lifetime he sold Bagatelle and many of the works of art that he had received in Lady Wallace's will. On his death he left the considerable collection still remaining at the rue Laffitte apartment to his friend Lady Sackville of Knole. She sold this *en bloc* to the Parisian dealer Seligmann and works of art from this collection can now be found in museums and private collections throughout the world.

Hertford House

Hertford House was built as Manchester House in 1776–88 for the 4th Duke of Manchester. It was designed by Joshua Brown and was then much smaller than it is today, comprising only five bays, with a Venetian window rather than the present conservatory on the first floor.

After a brief spell as the Spanish Embassy, it was leased in 1797 by the 2nd Marquess of Hertford who was attracted by the good duckshooting available in the area. It was the 2nd Marquess who added the conservatory as well as two first-floor rooms on each wing. The Prince Regent, drawn by his infatuation for the 2nd Marchioness and his friendship with the 3rd Marquess, was a frequent visitor in the decade before his accession to the throne in 1820.

Manchester House, later Hertford House, 1813

12

The Long Picture Gallery (now Gallery 22), *c.*1890

The house was leased as the French Embassy in 1836–51. But after 1851, under the 4th Marquess, it became little more than a store for his ever growing collection. In 1872 Sir Richard Wallace commissioned the architect Thomas Ambler to undertake a major programme of alterations: an inner quadrangle was created with stabling, coach-houses and a Minton-tiled smoking room on the ground floor and top-lit galleries on the first floor; the wings of the house were raised to the full height of the central block, and the façade was refaced with red brick. Today the galleries added by Ambler have parquet floors while the eighteenth-century part of the building is carpeted (the design copied from Wallace's original first-floor carpet).

In 1897–1900 the house was converted into a public museum. Exhibition galleries replaced the stabling, coach-houses and smoking room as well as some private rooms on the first floor. Many less radical changes have been made since then, notably the major refurbishment and installation of air-conditioning in 1976–82.

With the exception of the two great Caffiéri chandeliers in Galleries 4 and 16, all the chandeliers date from the nineteenth and twentieth centuries (although a few contain some eighteenth-century glass).

A Brief Visit to the Collection

The following dates of
French rulers may be useful:

Louis XIII	1610–43
Louis XIV	1643–1715
Régence	1715–23
Louis XV	1723–74
Louis XVI	1774–92
Napoleon I	1804–15
Louis XVIII	1815–24
Charles X	1824–30
Louis-Philippe	1830–48
Napoleon III	1852–70

For those visitors only able to make a brief visit, the medieval and Renaissance works of art and the armouries are on the ground floor, and French eighteenth-century art and old master paintings are on the first floor. Gallery 22 contains the principal masterpieces (including Hals' *The Laughing Cavalier*), while superb pieces of the eighteenth-century French art for which the Collection is best known are in Gallery 24. Some of the finest Sèvres porcelain can be found in Gallery 16, and the great collection of Dutch and Flemish paintings is concentrated in Galleries 18 to 21.

Explanation

In a guide of this kind it is only possible to include a selection of the finest works of art in each Gallery. Detailed discussions of almost all the works of art in the Collection may be found in the relevant catalogues.

All references to individual items are accompanied by their inventory numbers to facilitate their identification and to accord with the catalogues. Those catalogues currently available are listed on p.93.

The function of each Gallery in the time of Sir Richard Wallace and other relevant information about the fittings in his time have been indicated in italics after the Gallery headings.

The first-floor landing of Hertford House

Entrance Hall

(The present staircase was installed in 1872–5;
for the balustrade, see p.45)

English portraits

HOPPNER: *George IV as Prince of Wales* (P563)

This portrait was painted in about 1792 when the Prince
was thirty years old (a portrait of him by Lawrence in
Gallery 22 shows him thirty years later as King). In 1810 it
was given by the Prince (who specially commissioned the
frame) to the 3rd Marquess of Hertford, his Vice-
Chamberlain and sale-room adviser. The Prince at that
time was also enjoying a liaison with the 2nd Marchioness
of Hertford.

Gallery 1

(Formerly the Breakfast Room)

Bonington and early 19th-century paintings

BONINGTON

Richard Parkes Bonington, a brilliant but short-lived
talent, moved with his family from Nottingham to France
in 1817, and spent most of his short life in Paris. He was a
close friend of DELACROIX – whose *Faust and Mephistopheles*

Bonington *Sunset in the Pays de Caux* (P708)

(P324) hangs here, an illustration comparable with Bonington's *Child at Prayer* (P270) and *Anne Page and Slender* (P333). There are excellent examples of Bonington's romantic and anecdotal histories, such as *Henri III* (P323), and his freshly observed landscapes, such as *On the Coast of Picardy* (P341) and *A Sea Piece* (P273), one of his earliest oils.

Corridor

In the adjoining corridor is a selection of watercolours by BONINGTON, and by TURNER, who had a considerable influence on him. Bonington frequently added bodycolour with gum varnish over the darker areas, emulating the effect of an oil painting. *A Lady dressing her Hair* (P679) is an outstanding interior scene, while *Rouen* (P704) and *Sunset in the Pays de Caux* (P708) are particularly fine landscapes.

Gallery 2

(Formerly the Billiard Room)

Furniture, paintings and sculpture from the Louis XIV and Régence periods

FRENCH SCHOOL *c.*1715–20: *Madame de Ventadour with portraits of Louis XIV and his Heirs* (P122)

P122 portrays the whole Bourbon dynasty: the bust on the left, Henri IV (1553–1610); the bust on the right, his son, Louis XIII (1601–43); seated, Louis XIII's eldest son, Louis XIV (1638–1715); standing left, Louis XIV's eldest son, Louis, the Grand Dauphin (1661–1711); standing right, his eldest son, Louis, duc de Bourgogne (1682–1712); and the latter's only surviving son, the infant duc d'Anjou, later Louis XV (1710–74). The other figure is Madame de Ventadour, the duc d'Anjou's governess, who saved his life during an epidemic of smallpox in 1712. The picture was probably painted for her. Nearby is a Habsburg dynastic portrait, of the *Empress Maria Theresa and her family* (P758).

Coysevox *Le Brun* (S60)

COYSEVOX: *Charles Le Brun* (S60)

Le Brun (1619–90) was for many years a commanding figure in the French Academy. He was president in 1679 when Coysevox was admitted, the latter having offered as his reception piece a marble bust for which this terracotta (itself exhibited before the Academy in 1676) was the

French School *c.*1715–20 *Madame de Ventadour with portraits of Louis XIV and his Heirs* (P122)

model. Coysevox had been *sculpteur du Roi* since 1666, and was extensively employed at the various royal châteaux. His fine bronze **bust** of *Louis XIV* (S165), also in this room, dates from *c.*1699.

BOULLE furniture

André-Charles Boulle was the most celebrated *ébéniste* (cabinet-maker) working under Louis XIV, perfecting (though not inventing) the technique of brass and tortoise-shell marquetry associated with his name. The impressive **wardrobe** (F61) of *c.*1695, similar to F62 in Gallery 4, can be firmly attributed to the Boulle workshop. The central door-panels are veneered with *première-partie* marquetry (brass inlaid in tortoiseshell) and mounted with gilt-bronze groups of *Apollo and Daphne* (left) and *The Flaying of Marsyas* (right). The rigorous symmetry of the piece is emphasised by the repetition on the inner edges of the

Attributed to A.-C. Boulle Wardrobe (F61)

hinge-mounts, whose *fleurs de lis* suggest a royal provenance (the royal monogram is also stamped behind the keyhole escutcheons).

The lovely **toilet mirror** (F50) was made in 1713 as part of a service for the duchesse de Berri. Later it passed to Charlotte, princesse de Chimay, whose arms it now bears. It was made in the Boulle workshop with the marquetry on the back after an engraving by Jean Berain, the King's designer, who popularised designs of *singeries* (monkeys, often dressed in clothes and imitating human actions) such as this.

Gallery 3
(Formerly the Dining Room)
Furniture, paintings and Sèvres porcelain from the Louis XV and Louis XVI periods

OUDRY: *The Dead Wolf* (P626) and
The Dead Roe (P630)

Oudry, who specialized in animal and game pieces in the Dutch and Flemish tradition, received many commissions from European courts. He also made numerous tapestry designs, becoming director of the manufactories of Beauvais (1734) and the Gobelins (1748). P626 and P630, both of 1721, were painted as a pair and are among his finest works. (For Oudry see also Gallery 14.)

NATTIER: *Mademoiselle de Clermont en sultane* (P456)

This painting, dated 1733, fancifully depicts Mademoiselle de Clermont (1697–1741) at her bath amid attendants and accessories in the Turkish style. It typifies the fashion for *turqueries* popular at that time in France (see also C.A VAN LOO *The Grand Turk giving a Concert to his Mistress* (P451) in this Gallery). Her husband, the duc de Joyeuse, was killed in a hunting accident within a few days of their marriage in 1724, and their tragic romance became the basis for a once popular novel, *Mlle de Clermont* by Madame de Genlis.

Sèvres porcelain Ice-cream Cooler (c478)

Sèvres porcelain

Under the influence of Madame de Pompadour, the French royal porcelain factory moved from Vincennes to Sèvres in 1756, and was bought by Louis XV in 1759. Until the secret ingredient (kaolin) of Chinese and Meissen hard-paste porcelain was discovered in the 1760s, Sèvres could only make the more vulnerable and costly soft-paste variety. Each piece had to be moulded or thrown, fired, and then fired again after separate applications of glaze, colours and gilding. All the Sèvres porcelain in this unrivalled museum collection of over 300 pieces was made between 1752 and 1794, representing the vast range of models and decorations of the eighteenth century.

The magnificent **wine** and **ice-cream coolers** (c475, c478–9) in case B were part of an 800-piece service in the neo-classical style made at vast expense for Empress Catherine II of Russia in 1778–9; over 2200 pieces had to be rejected after firing damage. The hard-paste **tea-service** (c407–13) decorated with unusual *chinoiserie* battle scenes, case B, was made in 1779. It was acquired by either the 2nd or the 3rd Marquess of Hertford. Garnitures

Sèvres porcelain Plaque (c506*a*) from Carlin *Table à pupitre* (F327)

of Sèvres porcelain vases often served as diplomatic gifts (partly to promote French craftsmanship): the **garniture** with jewelled enamelling (c334–6), case A, was given in this way by Louis XVI to Prince Henry of Prussia in 1784. At 63,000 francs, it was the 4th Marquess of Hertford's most expensive purchase of Sèvres porcelain.

CARLIN: *Table à pupitre* (F327)

As ingenious as it is beautiful, F327 combines a work, writing and reading-table, and is veneered with tulip-wood and mounted with five fine Sèvres **plaques** (c506) painted by BOUILLIAT in 1783. Concealed within are two drawers, a writing-slide at each side and a mechanism allowing the entire top to be raised and tilted to form a book-rest. As Carlin (*maître* 1766) died in 1785, this must have been one of his last pieces. He also made the Sèvres-mounted **secretaire** (F304), veneered with tulip and purple-woods, the central **plaque** (c502) again painted by BOUILLIAT and dated 1776.

Copy of the Roll-Top Desk 'Le Bureau du Roi Louis XV' (F460)

The magnificent original desk (now at Versailles) was begun by OEBEN (*ébéniste du Roi* 1754) and completed in 1769 by his pupil RIESENER (*ébéniste du Roi* 1774) for Louis XV. It was the first roll-top desk ever made and the most expensive piece of furniture produced in eighteenth-century France. It also established Riesener's reputation, even though Oeben was responsible for much of the design and details. F460 was commissioned by the 4th Marquess and copies the mid nineteenth-century appearance of the original: during the Revolution its royal emblems had been replaced by attributes of the Arts (in marquetry on the roll-top) and its royal ciphers by Wedgwood-style Sèvres plaques (at the sides).

Gallery 4
(Formerly the Back State Room)

Sèvres porcelain, fine Boulle furniture, and Spanish and Dutch 17th-century paintings

Attributed to DROST: *The Unmerciful Servant* (P86)

Although accepted as a fine work by Rembrandt in the nineteenth century, this picture is now attributed to his pupil Willem Drost. It probably shows the moment in the Parable of the Unmerciful Servant when the king condemns one of his servants who had heartlessly extracted a debt from another, although a different Biblical subject, the Centurion Cornelius, has also been suggested. Drost's *Portrait of a young Woman* (P61) can be seen in Gallery 18.

MURILLO: *The Marriage of the Virgin* (P14)

The calm and pious art of Murillo, who painted this picture in about 1670, reached the peak of its popularity in the nineteenth century. The 4th Marquess of Hertford had a particular fondness for the artist, buying thirteen pictures by him or his followers. The precise touch and clear colours of P14 are unusual in his work. More typical are the four paintings in Gallery 22, whose broader brushwork reflects Murillo's admiration for the great Venetian masters of the sixteenth century.

Murillo *The Marriage of the Virgin* (P14)

Sèvres porcelain

The **saucepans** (c448–9), case 1, are the only surviving examples of their particular model; they were made c.1752 at Vincennes but painted in 1759, at Sèvres. Their essentially rococo form, with scrolling handles, swirling foliage and shell motifs, may be contrasted with the more geometric, neo-classical design of the **vase** (c270) painted with 'Savoyard' scenes in case 2. Made c.1765–70, this depicts children around a magic-lantern peepshow, and a trophy of toys. Peasants from the Savoy Alps who brought such entertainments with them were a popular feature of fairs in the eighteenth century.

Sèvres porcelain Vase
(c270)

BOULLE: Wardrobe and Clock (F429)

F429, with its fine *contre-partie* marquetry (where the design is of shell inlaid in brass), can be securely attributed to Boulle since it corresponds with an *armoire* listed in his inventory of 1715. The important **mantel clock** (F93) opposite, also appears in this inventory.

CAFFIÉRI: Chandelier (F83)

Jacques Caffiéri, one of a long dynasty of prominent sculptors and *ciseleurs* (chasers of cast metal), was much employed in the latter capacity by the French Crown. F83 is stamped '*CAFFIÉRI A. PARIS 1751*', the year it was presented (together with F84 in Gallery 16) by Louis XV to his eldest daughter, Madame Louise-Elisabeth. It is an exceptional example of the rococo style, of which Caffiéri was a leading exponent.

Gallery 5

(Formerly the Front State Room)

18th & 19th-century English paintings, and French Louis XVI furniture

LAWRENCE: *Margaret, Countess of Blessington* (P558)

Painted in 1822, this portrait of a fashionable literary hostess is one of the artist's most compelling characterisations. Byron, whom the Countess later met in Italy, wrote that it had 'set all London raving' when first exhibited. The Countess (who had lived briefly in Manchester Square) was obliged to sell all her possessions in 1849, and died shortly afterwards in Paris.

Lawrence *Margaret, Countess of Blessington* (P558)

Joubert Corner Cupboard
(F273)

JOUBERT: Corner Cupboards (F273–4)

This pair of *encoignures* was made in 1773 for the Versailles apartments of the comte d'Artois, whose military aspirations are reflected in the decoration of the pieces. His coat of arms was probably effaced from the gilt-bronze shields at the time of the Revolution. Joubert was a prolific maker of furniture for the court and was appointed *ébéniste du Roi* at the age of seventy-four in 1763.

Gallery 6

(Formerly two rooms: the Canaletto Room and the Sixteenth Century Room)

Medieval, Renaissance and Baroque works of art

Almost all the objects shown in Galleries 6 and 7 were collected by Sir Richard Wallace. His taste reflects the later nineteenth-century revival of the princely Renaissance enthusiasm for displaying together curiosities and works of art of a widely disparate nature.

PILON: *Charles IX of France* (s154)

Pilon, whose style reflects Italianate influences, was perhaps the most important sculptor of late sixteenth-century France; as *sculpteur du Roi*, he worked on many royal commissions. In this superb bronze bust Charles IX (1550–74) is lent dignity and status by the classical laurel-wreath and armour *à l'antique* – in reality he was feeble and undistinguished.

Wax miniatures (case 2)

Wax portraits and statuettes as works of art in their own right (rather than as models for cast bronzes) became popular in the courtly circles of France and Italy in the early sixteenth century. The diptych of the *Duc de Guise and his wife* (s417) which dates from that time is one of the earliest of its kind to survive. Later waxes include *Archduke Ernst of Austria* (s434) by ANTONIO ABONDIO, a late sixteenth-century Milanese medallist; *Ulrich, Grundherr von Altenthann und Weiherhauss* (s449) of 1627 by GEORG HOLDERMANN of Nuremberg; and *Susannah and the Elders* (s460) by DANIEL NEUBERGER of Augsburg (1621–80).

Illuminated manuscript cuttings (case 3)

These were cut from medieval and Renaissance manuscripts and framed in the nineteenth century. They range in date from the Pisan **initials** (M344), of the 1330s, to the French mid sixteenth-century *Garden of Love* scene (M323). Of particular quality are *Galeazzo Sforza in prayer* (M342), by CRISTOFORO DA PREDA (Milan, 1477), and the two scenes from *Boëthius* (M320–1), attributed to the MAÎTRE DE COËTIVY (French, 1460s).

Limoges painted enamels (case B)

The process of painted enamelling was invented at Limoges in the late-fifteenth century. The copper object was covered with a ground of enamel (a type of leaded glass), fired once, and then the different colours were each painted on and fired separately. The brilliance of the colours was often enhanced by the use of metal foil beneath the translucent enamel. Leading painters of the sixteenth century included the PÉNICAUD family, LÉONARD LIMOUSIN, PIERRE REYMOND and JEAN DE COURT – all represented here. Their designs were generally closely copied from contemporary engravings and woodcuts (see, for example, the

Limoges enamel
Parnassus Dish
(III F 268)

series of 24 **plaques** (III F 250) after Dürer's *Small Passion*
woodcuts). Especially attractive are the impressive *Parnassus* dish (III F 268) by MARTIAL COURTOIS, and the charming
tazza (III F 267) depicting *Noah's Ark* by JEAN DE COURT.

TORRIGIANO: *Head of Christ* (S7)

Pietro Torrigiano, who had been a student with Michelan-
gelo in the Florentine Academy, produced effigies of Henry
VII and his queen for Westminster Abbey in 1511–18.
This bust was also sculpted for the Abbey, and was
originally mounted on a wall between the Islip and
Esteney Chapels in the north transept. It was probably
removed from this location in the eighteenth century.

FOPPA: *The Young Cicero Reading* (P538)

Painted *c*.1464 by the principal Lombard artist of the time,
this is the only surviving fresco from the Palazzo Mediceo,
Milan (acquired by Cosimo de' Medici in 1455). It was set
in an open courtyard for four hundred years before being
cut down and framed, hence its poor condition. Cicero, the
great Roman orator, had excelled at school, and this
choice of subject reflects the Renaissance interest in
classical learning.

Glass Chalice
(xxv b 96)

Glass (case c)

Most pieces in the Collection were made in Venice, or in the Venetian manner, in the sixteenth and seventeenth centuries. The principal techniques using colourless glass (*cristallo*), opaque white canes (*vetro a filigrana*), mould-blowing and ice-glass are represented, and there is a good range of decorative methods, including enamelling, gilding, engraving and applied reliefs. Three particularly fine sixteenth-century pieces are the 'chalcedony' **goblet** (xxv b 92), a puzzle **tazza** (xxv b 72) with a mould-blown lion (both Venetian), and the French chalice-form **glass** (xxv b 96). The earliest object is the Syrian **mosque lamp** (xxv b 94), probably dating from the 1350s.

Gallery 7

(Formerly the Smoking Room; until 1937, Minton-tiled throughout)

Medieval, Renaissance and Baroque works of art

Coins and medals (case 1)

PISANELLO, who designed the medal of *Gianfrancesco Gonzaga* (s328), *c.*1444, was the first medallist since the classical period, and one of the greatest. Other important portrait medals include: *Sigismondo Malatesta* (s329) by MATTEO DEI PASTI (Verona, 1446); *Desiderius Erasmus* (s401) by MASSYS (Antwerp, 1519); and *The Emperor Charles V* (s400) by DÜRER (Nuremberg, 1521).

Earthenwares and stonewares (cases A, B and C)

Sixteenth and seventeenth-century pieces from Italy, Spain, France, Germany and Turkey. The two large **oval dishes** (c173–4) with wriggling grass snakes, shells, leaves and other creatures are typical works by BERNARD PALISSY (1510–90). They are of earthenware with a transparent polychrome lead glaze. **Hispano-Moresque** pieces include the large **dish** (c1), incorporating the early fifteenth-century arms of the Dukes of Burgundy, made in Valencia of tin-glazed earthenware decorated with a metallic lustre.

The Collection is particularly rich in Italian **maiolica**, which probably evolved from imported Hispano-Moresque wares in the early fifteenth century. The distinctive colours of these pieces are the result of firing pigments

Maiolica Dish with
The Triumph of Alcyone
(c89)

Fonduli *Seated Nymph*
(s72)

made from metallic oxides on to an opaque white tin-glaze
ground. The painters of vessels and dishes with figural
scenes (*istoriato* wares) copied the designs from engravings
after the great Renaissance masters. Especially magnificent examples are: the *Triumph of Alcyone* **dish** (c89) by
FRA XANTO AVELLI (Urbino, 1533); the vast **wine-cooler**
(c107), also made in Urbino, in 1574, perhaps for Cosimo I
de' Medici (his personal badge of a turtle with mast and
sail can be seen on the inner rim); and the *Bath of Maidens*
dish (c66) by MAESTRO GIORGIO ANDREOLI (Gubbio, 1525).

Sculpture

The large and fine pair of bronze fire-dogs on pedestals,
representing *Jupiter victorious over the Titans* (s161) and *Juno
controlling the winds* (s162), belonged to the Grand Dauphin
(eldest son of Louis XIV), and were later at Versailles.
They are by M. ANGUIER after designs by the great Italian
sculptor Algardi. Two rare and beautiful pieces in case 2
are the bronze *Seated Nymph* (s72) thought to be by
GIOVANNI FONDULI (Padua, sixteenth century), and the
boxwood *Hercules* (s273) signed by FRANCESCO DA SANT'
AGATA (Padua, 1520).

Jewellery Hat-badge
with *Judith and the Head
of Holofernes* (XII A 62)

Jewellery Hare-shaped
Pendant (XII A 78)

Renaissance jewellery (case 3)

Renaissance jewellery is notable for its use of faceted gems, fine enamelling, pendant forms and secular subjects; in character it is quite different from its classical or Gothic predecessors. The first and finest Renaissance jewels came from late fifteenth-century Italy but the new style, encouraged by the development of more ostentatious fashions in dress, spread rapidly throughout Europe. It persisted into the seventeenth century, and was much imitated in the nineteenth, making the identification of date and origin extremely hazardous. Particularly fine are the **hare-shaped pendant** (XII A 78), German late sixteenth century, an exquisite example of the taste for mounting large, irregularly shaped 'baroque' pearls; and the **hat-badge** (XII A 62) enamelled with *Judith and the Head of Holofernes*, a rare English work of *c*.1525.

The stairs lead up to Gallery 21.

Back Corridor

Italian earthenware; 18th & 19th-century works of art

Italian earthenware

The **dish** (C10), case A, featuring two young men is of incised (*a sgraffio*) slipware, the design having been scratched through a 'slip' of wet cream-coloured clay. This piece probably dates from the late fifteenth century, but could have come from a number of locations in northern Italy, where slipware was most popular. Examples of

maiolica from all the major centres, including Urbino, Gubbio, Faenza, Deruta, Cafaggiolo and Castel Durante, are shown. Urbino is well represented by the two Cupid **plates** (c109 and c110), case B, part of a sizeable dinner service probably made by the PATANAZZI workshop for the marriage of the Duke of Ferrara to Margarita Gonzaga in 1579.

Silver

Most notable among the small range of silversmiths' work in the Collection is the elegant French **ewer** (XII LC 192), case F, made in 1756 by SOMMEVERT. Its transitional *Régence* style, combining a relatively sober shape with less restrained decoration, can be explained at this date by its provincial origin (perhaps Soissons). Its function as a water container is shown by the bulrush and shell motifs; as a toilet item, it would probably have had a matching basin.

Galleries 8, 9 & 10

The bulk of the European armoury was assembled in 1871 by Sir Richard Wallace (see Introduction), who thereby created one of the finest collections in the world. It is particularly rich in finely decorated armours, sixteenth and seventeenth-century swords and decorated firearms. The collection is arranged in a roughly chronological order, with the earliest pieces in Gallery 10 and the later examples in Gallery 8.

Gallery 8

Renaissance arms and armour, firearms and edged weapons 16th to 19th century

Edged weapons

In addition to the fine displays of sixteenth and seventeenth-century swept-hilt **rapiers**, there are some very fine eighteenth-century **'dress' swords** and **small-swords** (mainly in case 5); these include one (A672) with an exceptional chiselled and gilt hilt by CASPAR SPÄT, who worked for the Bavarian court. Case H contains several later seventeenth-century civilian swords, the style of which marks the transition between the rapier and small-sword. A particularly interesting military weapon is the

Spanish **fighting sword** (A695), in case F, inscribed 'San Josef Feby.14 1797', indicating that it was probably surrendered from the warship of that name when the latter was captured by Horatio Nelson at the Battle of Cape St Vincent. Among the fine range of **daggers** are some exotic specialized examples such as spring-loaded triple-bladed **left-hand daggers**, and saw-toothed '**sword-breakers**' (case A, right). There are also a number of sixteenth-century **'Landsknecht' daggers**, named after a ferocious and flamboyant class of German mercenaries; one of their fearsome **two-handed swords** (A470) is in case B. The nearby '*Sword of Justice*' (A721) is of the type used as a 'heading sword', and in a ceremonial role would have symbolized the authority of judges over life and death. Some of the decorated weapons (especially the **hunting swords** and **knives** in case 6) were intended less for use than as works of art; particularly splendid is that given by Napoleon III to the 4th Marquess of Hertford (A707), in case 4.

Sadeler and Borstorffer Sporting Gun (A1090) detail

Projectile weapons

Many of the predominantly sixteenth-century **wheel-lock firearms** were obtained by Sir Richard Wallace from the enterprising Parisian dealer Frédéric Spitzer, who specialized in assembling or re-decorating such weapons to suit the taste of his wealthy clientele (see case 1). Outstanding among the unaltered wheel-lock guns is the magnificent **sporting gun** (A1090) in case 2 by DANIEL SADELER of Munich, with a stock by HIERONYMOUS BORSTORFFER, which was probaby made for the Electoral court. The **pistol** by JEAN LE BOURGEOIS (A1176) in case 2, and the **wheel-lock guns** in case 2 (A1110) and in case A (A1111), all came from the Armoury of Louis XIII, a noted gun-collector. Many of the important group of fine quality eighteenth-century guns in case 4 also have an impressive provenance: the silver-mounted **flint-lock blunderbuss** (A1124), made by J. A. GRECKE of St Petersburg in 1780, bears the monogram of Catherine the Great; and the magnificent **French sporting guns** by BOUTET (A1128–9) were once owned by Charles IV of Spain, but were seized by his usurper Joseph Bonaparte (who applied his coat of arms to one of them). Some of the many pistols in case 5 are similarly important; one pair of especially ornate **flint-lock pistols** (A1209–10) was made for Louis XIV as a gift from the City of Lille to mark French military successes in the Spanish Netherlands.

Armour

In the centre of the gallery is the impressive blacked, etched and gilt **equestrian harness** (A29) made by Hans Ringler of Nuremberg for Otto Heinrich, Count Palatine of the Rhine (1502–59); it is in fact composed of pieces from more than one 'garniture' (see Gallery 9). Most of the other armours in the wall cases date from the sixteenth and early seventeenth centuries. The late sixteenth-century Nuremberg black and white **munition armours** (A40–2) were worn by ordinary soldiers, and the series of **'morion' helmets** of similar date (A114–8), in case G, were made for the Saxon Electoral Guard. The increasing effectiveness of firearms in battle led to the gradual abandonment of full plate armour; the **'cuirassier' armour** (A65) in case H, South German, c.1620, marks its final form. The small dent in the $11\frac{1}{4}$lbs (5kg) breastplate is a mark of the proof of that piece against shot. The richly etched and gilt Italian **armour** (A63) of c.1600–10 in case E, although of similar form, was made as a parade armour for a Prince of the House of Savoy; its breastplate, weighing only $7\frac{3}{4}$lbs (3.5kg), would not have been shot-proof.

Works of art

The very fine walnut **coffer** in case A, inlaid with stag's horn, mother of pearl and brass (A1345), is signed by the Alsatian gunstock-maker J.-C. TORNIER, and dated 1630. He probably made and decorated the stock of the **wheel-lock rifle** (A1099) in case 2, dated 1645.

South and Horn Sword of Henry, Prince of Wales (A511) detail

Gallery 9
Renaissance arms and armour

Edged weapons

In case 1 is a very fine combined **wheel-lock pistol** and **swept-hilt rapier** (A1241) made in Augsburg *c.*1580–90. Most of the swords in the Collection are German or Italian, but the hilt of the silver-encrusted **cross-hilted sword** (A511) in case 4 is English, probably by ROBERT SOUTH of London (although its blade is by the German CLEMENS HORN). This rare dress sword was made for Henry, Prince of Wales (d.1612), who predeceased both his father, James I, and his younger brother, Charles I.

During the seventeenth century in Spain, and to a certain extent in Spanish-dominated Italy also, the **'cup-hilted' rapier** became fashionable in place of the earlier 'swept' form; a superb example (A655) in case 2, dated 1701, has a fine chiselled hilt by ESTRADA of Madrid, and a blade by FRANCISCO GOMEZ of Toledo. In case H are several ornately pierced and chiselled Spanish or Italian **left-hand daggers** (swords were usually held in the right hand, daggers in the left). More common in Northern Europe were **'quillon' daggers**; a particularly notable one in case 3 (A790) was given to Henri IV of France by the City of Paris upon the occasion of his marriage to Marie de Médicis in 1600; its companion rapier (now in the Musée de l'Armée, Paris) was carried by Napoleon on his campaigns throughout Europe as a symbol of good luck.

'Quillon' Dagger
of Henri IV of France
(A790)

35

Mazzaroli Cannon Barrel (A1245) with carriage

Projectile weapons

Especially fine is the cast and chased bronze **cannon barrel** (A1245), signed and dated 1688 by F. MAZZAROLI of Venice. Its impressive carriage was made in the nineteenth century for Prince Anatole Demidoff, at whose sale in 1870 it was bought by the 4th Marquess of Hertford.

Armour

The Gothic **harness** for man and horse (A21) dominates this room; although restored in the nineteenth century and partly composite, its elegant form and shell-like fluting are characteristic of German fifteenth-century armour at its best. It was probably made for a member of the Bavarian von Freyberg family c.1470–90. The sixteenth-century armour ranges in date from the German 'Maximilian' style (A24) in case B to the richly ornamented Italian parade armour (A51) in case F. The three Augsburg **tilt armours** (A47–9) in case G, made in the late 1580s, are probably all from the workshop of ANTON PEFFENHAUSER.

Garnitures

In the sixteenth century it became fashionable to build one armour to which 'exchange' pieces could be added, substituted or removed, either to alter its function (between war, parade, and various forms of the tournament) or as reinforcement. Over the centuries many such garnitures have been dispersed, and several very fine pieces are now in this Collection. In case 4 there is an etched and

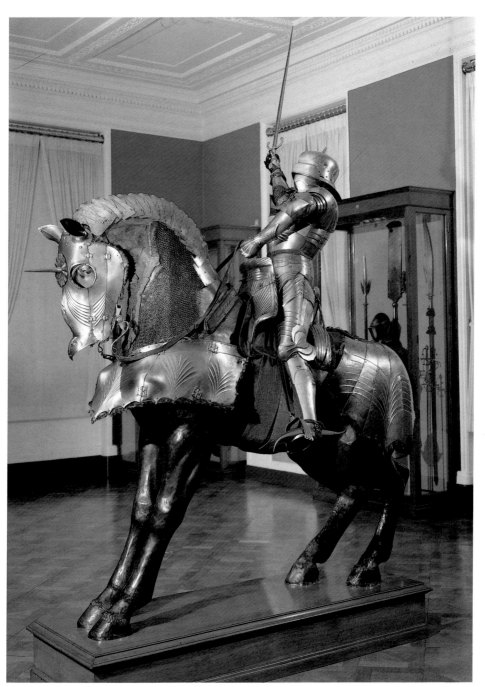

Gothic Harness for man and horse (A21)

gilt **helmet** for tournament on foot (A188) from the 'Golden Garniture' made for the Emperor Ferdinand I in 1555. Adjacent are the **helmet, pauldron** (shoulder armour) and **vamplate** (for the lance) from an Augsburg garniture made *c*.1575 for the Emperor Maximilian II's two sons (A187, A242, A343). A **gauntlet** (A270) is part of another Augsburg garniture, made for Maximilian in 1550 by MATTHÄUS FRAUENPREIS and etched by JÖRG SORG. A further garniture made for Maximilian, in 1571, is represented by a **shaffron** (headpiece for a horse) (A359) and **vamplate** (A342). The **embossed shield** (A320), from a garniture made *c*.1556–9 for Henri II, is French, with decoration after designs by ETIENNE DELAUNE; while a right-hand **gauntlet** (A276) was made *c*.1608 at Greenwich (probably by JACOB HALDER) for Henry, Prince of Wales. The only complete harness of English plate armour here is in case C (A62), the superb Greenwich **field garniture** made *c*.1587 probably for Thomas Sackville, Lord Buckhurst.

Gallery 10
Medieval and Renaissance arms and armour

Edged weapons

The display in case C illustrates, from right to left, the development of the **sword** from the simple cross-hilt as in the tenth-century North European example (A456), to the sixteenth-century 'developed' hilt, such as A480 with its more complex guard. Especially fine are the Renaissance swords and daggers in case 2 in the centre of the Gallery: the **sword** (*falchion*) A710 came from the Armoury of the Medici. The **dagger** A743, is one of a number of rare fifteenth-century Italian *cinquedea* (having blades of 'five fingers' breadth); it retains its original sheath of *cuir bouille* (tooled hardened leather).

Many of the arms have a noble provenance. In case 1, for example, there is the fifteenth-century **serving-knife** (A881) of Philip the Good, Duke of Burgundy, richly enamelled with his coat of arms. There is also an impressive range of staff weapons, of which the finest is probably the **polaxe** (A926) in case C, made *c*.1450–70. The motto 'de bon' in a heart (i.e. 'of good heart') is incised into the decorative brass inlay of the head. Polaxes such as this were commonly used in tournaments when fighting on foot, but no doubt were also used in battle.

Crossbow (A1032)

Projectile weapons

In case 1 is a magnificent late fifteenth-century **crossbow** (A1032) which once belonged to the Völs Colonna family in the Tyrol. The tiller is overlaid with plaques of carved staghorn to resemble ivory, while the bow is in steel (an early example of its use) covered with painted and gilded parchment. A weapon as fine as this would have been used for ostentatious display in the hunt, rather than for war. Later crossbows are in Gallery 8 (case A), together with a selection of bolts or quarrels, as their arrows were called.

Armour

Particularly fine and rare pieces of armour in this Gallery include the Milanese **basinet** (helmet) made c.1390–1410 (A69), case 4, and the pair of late fourteenth-century hour-glass **gauntlets** (A251–2), case 3, with incised decoration incorporating the motto 'Amor' (Love). Of similar rarity, made from only two pieces of entirely hand-forged iron, is the fifteenth-century frog-mouthed **great helm** (A186) in the same case. Nearby in case F is the heaviest **tilt armour** (A23) in the Collection, weighing 96lbs (43kg). It dates from the early sixteenth century, and was possibly made for the Nuremberg tournaments, its surface bearing ample evidence of its use. Armour like this was quite unsuited for war; a lighter **armour**, more appropriate for the battle-field but, with the addition of exchange pieces, also suitable for use at a tournament, stands next to it (A22) in case G. It was probably made for Wladislas, King of Poland and

Basinet (A69)

Hungary, *c.*1510. Later Renaissance armour fashioned in a more ornate style is also to be found here (and in Gallery 9). The **visor** (A204) in case B, embossed into the form of a grotesque Turk's face, is from a parade helmet made for the future Emperor Ferdinand I in 1529. The Italian **parade helmets** in case 2 are of a similar date and are attributed to famous craftsmen such as the NEGROLI BROTHERS of Milan and CAREMOLO MODRONE of Mantua.

The stairs lead to Gallery 23.

Mughal Indian Dagger (OA1409)

Gallery 11

Oriental arms, armour and works of art. Also French Orientalist paintings

Nearly all the Oriental arms, armour and works of art were acquired by the 4th Marquess of Hertford in 1860–70, a period when objects of this kind were highly fashionable in Parisian society. They were regarded as suitable for wall displays and as works of art.

Edged weapons

Most of the edged weapons are Indian and Persian, with some Turkish and Far Eastern examples in cases C and G. Of special interest are the daggers in case 6, particularly the jewelled and gold-hilted Mughal Indian **dagger** (OA1409) dating from the early seventeenth century, and

Indian Tulwar of Tipu Sultan (OA1402)

the Persian example (OA1414) with its gold encrusted blade dated 1496–7. The fine collection of swords includes an Indian **tulwar** once owned by Tipu Sultan of Mysore (OA1402) in case B; its jade hilt is inlaid with gold, diamonds, rubies and emeralds, and its fine seventeenth-century Persian blade bears the badge of Tipu (a tiger) damascened in gold. Also worth noting is the superb fifteenth-century Japanese **sword blade** (OA1694) in case F.

Armour

The armour is predominantly eighteenth and nineteenth-century Indian and Persian, of steel decorated with gold in a technique known as *cuftgari*, in which the gold is applied and burnished on to a finely cross-hatched ground. In Europe this work was known as 'counterfeit damascening' because the gold was not laid into a groove cut to receive it, as in 'true' damascening. Especially impressive is the nineteenth-century Imperial **court dress** of a Chinese Mandarin (OA1701) in case A, flanked by two standing figures illustrating the war panoply of late eighteenth and nineteenth-century warriors, that on the left North Indian, that on the right Persian. Also in this Gallery is displayed the **war panoply** of an Indian Rajput warrior (OA1790–4). This includes a rare late eighteenth-century 'Coat of Ten Thousand Nails', so-called because of its many gilt studs. Few similar pieces have survived because of the fragility of the textile elements.

Projectile weapons

Displayed in cases D and E, the richly decorated matchlock and flintlock firearms were designed not only for conspicuous display and as prestigious gifts for Eastern potentates but often also for use. The **matchlock carbine** (OA2202), case E, with a hand-turned cylinder capable of holding six charges was made in India in the late-seventeenth century. The unusual eighteenth-century **matchlock gun** (OA2003) from Bhutan is a purpose-designed hunting weapon, fitted with a hinged bi-pod support for steady, accurate shooting. In contrast, the **flintlock blunderbuss** (OA2086), case D, can only have been used for show; its touch-hole has never been drilled, and it therefore cannot be fired.

Works of art

Of special note in case 6 is the rare Indian or Persian **dish and cover** (OA1662) of richly enamelled gold, signed in Persian by the maker and dated 1811. The West African **Asante gold treasure** (OA1673–83), in the centre of the gallery, case 4, was bought by Sir Richard Wallace, probably following a charitable auction for the widows and orphans of soldiers who fought in the 1874 Asante campaign.

VERNET: *The Arab Tale-teller* (P280)

French nineteenth-century interest in the land and culture of the Arabs was greatly stimulated by the conquest of Algeria in 1830. Vernet paid four visits to Algeria, where he understood the Arab way of life to be a survival from Biblical times (see *Judah and Tamar* (P346) and *Joseph's Coat* (P349) in Gallery 23). He also produced many Orientalist pictures without Biblical reference, of which the *Arab Tale-*

43

Vernet *The Arab Tale-teller* (P280)

teller, painted in 1833, was the first to be exhibited at the Salon. The 4th Marquess knew Vernet well and admired his works; there are twenty-nine of his oils and water-colours in the Collection.

DECAMPS: *The Turkish Patrol* (P307)

Turkish themes had been common in eighteenth-century French art (see Nattier's *Mademoiselle de Clermont* in Gallery 15) and they became part of a more general Oriental taste in the nineteenth century. Decamps visited the Middle East and North Africa in 1828 and thereafter painted numerous Oriental scenes, usually in a heavily impasted technique that has not lasted well. *The Turkish Patrol*, showing nine foot-patrolmen accompanying the chief of police on his round in Smyrna, was Decamps's first major Oriental subject. With Horace Vernet, he was one of the 4th Marquess of Hertford's favourite artists and there are twenty-eight of his paintings and watercolours in the Collection.

Gallery 12 Shop & Information

(Formerly the Housekeeper's Room)

19th-century English paintings

LANDSEER: *The Arab Tent* (P376)

Landseer and his animal paintings were particularly admired by Queen Victoria. This picture, painted in 1866, was bought directly from the artist by her son, the Prince of Wales (later Edward VII), and then from him by Sir Richard Wallace. At over £7,800, it was the most expensive work of art ever bought for the Collection.

Grand Staircase & Landing

Balustrade (F68)

This is perhaps the finest example of French iron and bronze work from the early Louis XV period to have survived. It was made in 1733–41 for the stairs in the *Bibliothèque du Roi* in the Palais Mazarin in Paris – hence the royal emblems of sunflowers and interlaced L's – probably after designs by ROBERT DE COTTE. It was sold as scrap-iron in *c*.1860, when its style was out of fashion, but was subsequently acquired by the 4th Marquess of Hertford and installed by Sir Richard Wallace in Hertford House in 1872–5.

Balustrade (F68) detail

45

BOUCHER: *The Rising of the Sun* (P485) and
The Setting of the Sun (P486)

This magnificent pair of mythological scenes, painted in
1753 and 1752 respectively, depict the sun god Apollo
attended by Tethys, wife of Oceanus, and the Nereids and
Tritons. In P485, Apollo is being prepared for his journey
across the sky to bring the day, preceded by Aurora
(crowned by the Morning Star) while *putti* push back the
night clouds. In P486, Apollo dismounts from his sun-
chariot at dusk, with the Evening Star above. These
paintings were in the collection of Madame de Pompadour
at her château of Bellevue by 1754 and the artist himself
regarded them as among his best works. Boucher's official
eminence was largely contrived by Pompadour's extensive
patronage (see her portrait in Gallery 25).

BOUCHER: *An Autumn Pastoral* (P482) and
A Summer Pastoral (P489)

Boucher painted these pendant scenes in 1749 for the
financier Trudaine's new château at Montigny-Lencoup.
Their subjects derive from *pantomimes* by his friend Favart
(for whom he sometimes devised theatrical settings). They
are his largest and arguably his finest theatrical pastorals.
Two other paintings derived from Favart's plays are in
Galleries 24 (P399) and 13 (P431). Three further pairs of
paintings by Boucher hang on the Landing.

Boucher *The Rising of the Sun* (P485)

Greuze *Innocence* (P384)

Gallery 13
(Formerly Lady Wallace's boudoir)

English and French paintings reflecting the 18th-century cult of sensibility. Louis XV and Louis XVI furniture

The sentimental and moral paintings of Jean-Baptiste Greuze provide a complete contrast to Boucher's decorative pleasures. They were intended to evoke tender feelings in the heart of the viewer and introduced a new sentimentality into French painting. Reynolds and Morland in Gallery 13 reflect the same attitude in eighteenth-century English painting. Reynolds in particular admired Greuze's pictures and they may have influenced some of his compositions.

GREUZE: *The Inconsolable Widow* (P454)
and *The Broken Mirror* (P442)

These two pictures were both painted in 1762–3 and offer examples of virtue and vice. The young widow rereads old letters and vows fidelity to her husband while her grieving dog lies at her feet. In *The Broken Mirror* the elaborate disorder of the room implies the intemperance of the girl, whose abject misery is shared by her startled dog.

GREUZE: *Innocence* (P384)

Innocence was the most expensive of the 4th Marquess of Hertford's French eighteenth-century paintings and long remained exceedingly popular (it was once the most reproduced picture from the Wallace Collection). Greuze's later work included many such sentimental heads, which particularly appealed to the 4th Marquess (there are thirteen in the Collection today, see also in Galleries 15 and 24). Such works enjoyed considerable success with an audience which did not share our present cynicism with the sentimental.

REYNOLDS: *The Strawberry Girl* (P40)

Reynolds' studies of children display a particular, avuncular affection for his young models which compares attractively with Greuze's more sensual approach. *The Strawberry Girl* shows one of his child models dressed up in character. Exhibited at the Royal Academy in 1773, the picture was regarded by Reynolds as one of his best works and the many repetitions produced in his studio testify to its popularity.

R. DUBOIS: Writing-table, inkstand and *cartonnier* (F330, F287 and F178)

All three pieces are lacquered with green *vernis Martin*, a substance made in imitation of Oriental lacquer using many coats of coloured varnish which (like Oriental lacquer itself) were rubbed down and polished after each application. The name derives from the brothers Martin who perfected but did not invent the process. These pieces were made in Paris c.1763, possibly for Catherine II of Russia.

WEISWEILER: Work-table (F325)

The early history of this work-table, for use by a lady engaged in sewing or some similar domestic occupation, is unknown. It was probably made in the 1780s, but it is first recorded in 1807 in the apartments of the Empress Josephine at the Tuileries in Paris. Its grace and delicacy reflect both its intended use and its date. Under Louis XVI lighter and smaller pieces of furniture for use by ladies became fashionable. The Wedgwood plaques were probably imported by the fashionable shopkeeper Daguerre, for whom Weisweiler frequently worked. Wedgwood's designs and products were popular and influential in France.

Corridor

In the two cases in the corridor between Galleries 13 and 14 are displayed, among other items, gold boxes, a perpetual almanach and a silver-gilt service.

Gold boxes

In the eighteenth century the taking of snuff was a fashionable activity enjoyed by women as well as men. Most of the gold boxes in the Collection were intended for snuff but they were also extravagant toys for the very rich, as much designed for display as for use. Superb works of craftsmanship, they kept their contents fresh only by the precision of the fit of box and lid, and do not have catches of any sort. They can also be held perfectly balanced in the hand with the lid raised.

Most of the gold boxes in the Collection are French but there are also examples from Germany, Austria, Switzerland and England. There are boxes decorated entirely in gold, either plain or four-colour (achieved by adding other metals like silver or iron to the gold), but most have painted decoration, either on enamel, gouache, gold foil or porcelain. Glass, Japanese lacquer, tortoiseshell and mother-of-pearl were also used. The 4th Marquess of Hertford bought some of the boxes, but most seem to have been acquired by Sir Richard Wallace.

One of the most interesting boxes, G80, made of gold and the hardstone cornelian, has a secret panel, rediscovered only in 1976, showing on each side gouache portraits of Voltaire and his mistress, Madame du Châtelet. It was made in Dresden in *c.*1770–75.

Gold box (G80) with *Portrait of Voltaire*

In the display case there are also some beautifully made drizzling shuttles, used for winding gold thread removed from dresses so that the gold could be used again.

MARTINIÈRE: Perpetual Almanach (F64)

This almanach in four parts was made for Louis XV in 1741–2. It is of enamel on copper, painted on a white ground, and framed with bronze. The slips indicate the days of the week and the phases of the moon as well as the date and names of the various feast days. The appropriate sign of the zodiac is also indicated. The back of each panel is removable to allow the slips to be adjusted annually.

Silver-gilt Service

This service was made (with its fitted leather case, not on display) by several craftsmen at Augsburg between 1757 and 1773. Comprising fifty-five pieces, the service can be divided into three parts: a toilet service, a table service, and a writing set. It may have been used by a man or a woman but the identity of the original owner is unknown.

Gallery 14

(Formerly Sir Richard Wallace's Study)

Fine Boulle furniture; paintings by Oudry and Desportes

BOULLE furniture

In the centre of the room stands a fine **writing-table** (F427) with gilt-bronze satyr's mask mounts at each corner. It was probably made in the Boulle workshop *c.*1700–10, a little before the superb **inkstand** (F49) which rests upon it. This was made in 1710 for the Paris Guild of Surgeons, whose motto and arms are incorporated within the elaborate marquetry design. Around the top edge are the names of some of the senior surgeons, including that of Georges Mareschal, who was first surgeon to Louis XIV. Phrases and symbols relating to medicine appear on the outer edges. The Boulle workshop also made the imposing **pedestal clock** (F42) mounted with figures representing the four continents of (from the left) Africa, Europe, Asia and America. The clock movement is by MYNUËL; other examples of this clock have an oval dial with hands that expand and contract correspondingly.

Attributed to A.-C. Boulle Inkstand (F49)

JACOB: Set of six arm-chairs and two sofas (F185–92)

These fine chairs and sofas are stamped with the mark of Georges Jacob, the most eminent chair-maker of the Louis XVI period. They are covered with Louis XV Beauvais tapestry, probably applied in the nineteenth century. The various scenes of animals are taken from designs by OUDRY, who in 1748 painted as overdoors the set of four animal subjects in this Gallery (P625, P627, P629 and P631).

Musical Clock (F97)

Probably designed by DUPLESSIS *père*, the fine gilt-bronze case of F97 was cast by MORLAY (*maître* 1756), and the clock movement made by VIGER (*maître* 1744). The carillon of fourteen bells, the mechanism of which was probably made by another craftsman, provides a sequence of thirteen different tunes, including that of *Baa Baa Black Sheep* (known in French as *Ah! Vous dirai-je, Maman*).

Riesener Roll-top
Desk (F102)

Gallery 15

*(Formerly the Oval Drawing Room; this is the only room to
retain its original fireplace)*

Late 18th-century French furniture, sculpture and paintings

RIESENER: Roll-top Desk (F102)

This superb desk was made by Riesener in 1769 for the
hôtel (town house) of Pierre Grimod, comte d'Orsay (1748–
1809), whose *OR* monogram appears in marquetry on
each side. Above the monograms appear the attributes of
warfare, perhaps in allusion to Orsay's position as an
officer in the dragoons. Other marquetry designs relate to
the function of the desk. While closely related in style to the
famous *bureau du Roi* (see Gallery 3), F102 is less elaborate in
detail, lacking the clock, candelabra and some other gilt-
bronze mounts. Riesener, who probably made the unusual
oval **secretaire** (F306) also in this room, was the most
versatile cabinet-maker of his time; other pieces by him can
be seen in Galleries 3, 13, and, particularly, 24.

Boulard Chair (F233)   Houdon *Madame Victoire de France* (s25)

BOULARD: Set of six chairs (F233–8)

Boulard, who worked regularly for the Crown from 1777, made these important chairs in 1786 for Louis XVI's card-room at Fontainebleau. They formed part of a larger set of thirty-five chairs, eight matching curtains and a screen, all with a blue and white silk *lampas* of the same design as that rewoven for F233–8 in 1982. Chairs with separate cushions, such as these, were intended for ladies. Their rather cool, but refined neo-classical design is typical of the taste of the court in its final years before the Revolution. The very fine gilt-bronze **wall-lights** (F374–7) belong to a model made both for Louis XV's daughter, Madame Adélaïde, at Versailles and for Marie-Antoinette at Saint-Cloud; both sets were cast by FELOIX in 1787.

HOUDON: *Madame Victoire de France* (s25) and *Madame de Sérilly* (s26)

The Revolution was to have a dramatic effect on the lives of the sculptor and the subjects of these two splendid busts. Madame Victoire (1733–99), the fifth daughter of Louis

55

XV, was forced to flee France in 1791 with her sister, Madame Adélaïde, and both died as refugees in Italy during the harsh winter of 1799–1800. In 1794, Madame de Sérilly (1763–?99) was accused, with twenty-three others (including her husband and his brother), of having plotted to assist the King. All but Madame de Sérilly were guillotined; she escaped on the unfounded belief that she was pregnant. Houdon, the culminating figure in the evolution of eighteenth-century French portrait sculpture, fell into relative obscurity with the collapse of the *ancien régime*. These works of 1777 (s25) and 1782 (s26) belong to the most successful decades of his career. (Several other important sculptures by Houdon were kept by Lord Hertford at Bagatelle and were later sold by Sir John Murray Scott.) Between them stands an urn-shaped **vase** (s32) with reliefs of infant Bacchanals by CLODION.

GREUZE: *Votive offering to Cupid* (P441)

Despite his success with sentimental genre, Greuze had serious ambitions as a history painter, the noblest category of painting according to the eighteenth-century hierarchy of subject matter maintained by the French Academy. This is one of several classical subjects he painted in the late 1760s, and the details of architecture, altar and ewer, reflect the then current 'grecian' vogue. Weaknesses in the drawing of the girl and the inconsistent perspective suggest Greuze may have been overreaching himself. The Academy was never to accept him as a history painter.

VIGÉE LE BRUN: *Madame Perregaux* (P457)

It is recorded that the artist was particularly satisfied with this lively portrait of Madame Perregaux (whose husband was banker to the 3rd Marquess of Hertford). The daughter of a portrait painter, the artist married the dealer J.-B.-P. Le Brun in 1776 and – until the fateful year of 1789, the date of this painting – their Paris *hôtel* was a centre of fashionable society. With the Revolution, she left France to practise with continued success in Italy, Vienna and St Petersburg, returning to Paris only in 1801.

Régulateur (Astronomical) Clock (F98) detail

Gallery 16
(Formerly the Large Drawing Room)

Sèvres porcelain, Boulle furniture and 17th to 19th-century landscapes

Régulateur (Astronomical) Clock (F98)

The monumental scale, elaborate decoration and complex movement of F98 make it one of the most remarkable clocks produced in eighteenth-century France. It was made *c.*1750 for the financier Jean-Paris de Monmartel (godfather to Madame de Pompadour), who was portrayed with it in an engraving of 1772. The movement was designed by FORTIER and made by STOLLEWERCK; the patinated-bronze figures are possibly by J. CAFFIÉRI (who

Sèvres porcelain Vase '*à tête d'éléphant*' (c246) detail

signed the fine **chandelier** (F84) in this room; see also Gallery 4). The principal clock-face now shows Greenwich mean time (blued-steel hand) and true solar time (gilt hand); from the central dial can be read the passage of the sun across the zodiac, the age, longitude and phases of the moon, and the time anywhere in the northern hemisphere (a map of which is engraved on the revolving circular plate); the two lower dials display the times of the rising and setting of the sun (left) and of the moon (right).

Sèvres porcelain: Vases '*à tête d'éléphant*' (C246–7)

Made in 1756, this pair of vases with candle holders typifies the extraordinary imagination and variety of the designers at the Sèvres factory, particularly its chief designer, JEAN-CLAUDE DUPLESSIS *père* (*c.*1695–1774). The delicate painting is by DODIN, perhaps the finest of the painters at Sèvres, who also may have painted the inkstand C488. Later models required the addition of supporting handles under the vulnerable trunks (see C249–50 in Gallery 12).

Sèvres porcelain: Inkstand (C488)

This remarkable inkstand, made in 1758, is one of only three of its design known today. The terrestial globe contained the inkwell, and the celestial globe the sand shaker (for drying ink). The cushion contained a cleaning-sponge, and a bell (now lost) was within the crown. It was

Sèvres porcelain Inkstand (c488)

almost certainly given by Louis XV to his third daughter, Marie-Adélaïde (1732–1800), whose *MA* monogram appears on one side. However, when the 4th Marquess of Hertford bought the piece in 1843, the monogram was implausibly interpreted as that of Marie-Antoinette (1755–93), who was said to have used the inkstand to write her farewells before being taken to the guillotine.

Sèvres porcelain: Toilet Service (c458–65)

This service, of the finest quality, may well have been intended for Madame de Pompadour as it was left incomplete shortly before her death in 1764. One would expect additional items such as boxes, cups, mirrors, ring stands and candlesticks. She was notoriously vain in her later years, and used extensive make-up in an attempt to maintain her beauty. The largest pair of pots were for hair powder of scented starch, airtight seals excluding both dampness and mites; the tall pair were for hair grease; and the smallest pair for the fashionable and suggestive black face patches. There is also a clothes brush and a small *vergette* for dusting wig powder from the shoulders.

Gallery 17

(Formerly the Small Drawing Room)

Canaletto and Guardi; Louis XV furniture

CANALETTO: *Two views of the Bacino, Venice* (P497 and P499)

Canaletto, whose work was highly favoured by English patrons, painted this impressive pair of complementary panoramas *c.*1740. They convey rather more than topography, for the ships and travellers from many nations also describe the business of Venice as a port. The pictures were acquired at an unknown date by the 1st Marquess of Hertford together with four other views by the artist (or from his studio) in Gallery 16 (P496, P500, P507 and P511).

GUARDI: *Four views of Venice* (P491, P494, P503 and P508)

These very fine views were painted as a set in the 1770s and in the earlier nineteenth century they were in a collection in St Petersburg. In contrast to Canaletto, whose primary concern was topographical, Guardi was more interested in capturing the light and atmosphere of the city. A further pair of views (P517, 518) and three architectural *capricci* (P502, 504 and 647) by Guardi are also in this Gallery.

MARCHAND: Cabinet (F70) and Chest of Drawers (F88)

F70 is one of a pair of cabinets made by Marchand in 1755 for Louis XV's bedchamber at Fontainebleau. Contemporary records indicate that it was originally decorated with lacquer; this presumably deteriorated, and was replaced by the present rosewood veneer. F88, also one of a pair, was made in the same year for the bedchamber at Fontainebleau of Queen Marie Leczinska, wife of Louis XV. It follows the design of F70, although the mounts are more elaborate and it retains its original lacquer. The bowed (*bombé*) front and sides, the Oriental lacquer, and the scrolling acanthus mounts are characteristic of rococo furniture.

CRESSENT: Cartel Clock (F92)

The *ébéniste* Charles Cressent was frequently fined by the guild authorities on suspicion of casting furnishing bronzes (such as clock cases and fire-dogs) thereby transgressing his limits as a cabinet-maker, and this clock was probably among works sold in 1749 to pay off his debts. The superb gilt-bronze case, featuring the figures of *Love triumphing over Time*, is certainly more like sculpture than furniture – to which Cressent may have made a small concession with the Boulle marquetry on the sides. The clock-mounted **cartonnier** (F72), modified in the nineteenth century, is also attributed to Cressent.

Gallery 18

(Formerly the East Drawing Room)

Dutch and Flemish paintings; Boulle furniture

DROST: *Portrait of a young Woman* (P61)

This painting of *c.* 1654 was recognized as by Rembrandt's pupil Drost as early as 1874, even though then (as now) very little was known about the artist. At the time it bore a false Rembrandt signature (since removed). BACKER: *Portrait of an elderly Woman* (P89) also once had a false

Rembrandt signature, although he was never a pupil, while BOL, who did study under the master *c.*1635–41, painted *The Toper* (P74). Another of Rembrandt's many pupils, FLINCK, painted *A Young Negro Archer* (P238), a fine example of the fashion for studies of exotically-dressed figures.

BOULLE: Console Table (F56)

This fine table, made *c.*1700–10, can be securely given to Boulle since a variant (the mounts with the heads and feet of rams rather than lions) was published *c.*1724 in a book of his designs. He was also responsible for the amusing and fanciful marquetry scene of monkeys on a tightrope, an early example of *singerie*, of which an expanded version can be seen on the side table (F425) stamped by Leleu in Gallery 19. Both were derived from models originally designed for the little Château de la Ménagerie at Versailles.

VAN HUYSUM: *Flowers in a Vase* (P149)

Van Huysum painted this immaculate display in 1726. As the flowers, which include varieties of crown imperial, hyacinth, anemone, tulip, rose, jasmine and veronica, are of different seasons, the artist may have painted the picture over an extended period as the various flowers came into bloom.

Gallery 19

(Built in 1872–5 for Sir Richard Wallace's Oriental Armoury)

Dutch and Flemish 17th-century paintings; Boulle furniture

J. VAN RUISDAEL: *Rocky Landscape* (P50)

The looming rocks and diminutive figures lend a sombre character to this landscape, a comparatively early work by Ruisdael, perhaps the greatest of the many seventeenth-century Dutch landscape painters. Fine landscapes by his pupil, HOBBEMA, by WIJNANTS, and by EVERDINGEN, whose work may have influenced Ruisdael, also hang in this room. One of Hobbema's masterpieces, *A Stormy Landscape* (P75), is in Gallery 22.

Rubens *The Triumphal Entry of Henri IV into Paris* (P522)

RUBENS: oil sketches (P519–24)

Rubens was a remarkably prolific artist who produced many oil sketches either in preparation for large-scale paintings or as tapestry designs. *The Defeat and Death of Maxentius* (P520) is an example of the latter, one of a series of twelve scenes illustrating the life of the Roman Emperor Constantine the Great. The two sketches of the *Adoration of the Magi* are *modelli* for well-known altarpieces in Antwerp (P519) and (now) King's College, Cambridge (P521), and were painted in 1624 and 1633 respectively. Most impressive of all in their freshness and vivacity, are the three sketches (P522–4) of 1628 relating to a cycle of paintings glorifying the *Life of Henri IV*. This was commissioned by the subject's widow, Marie de Médicis (whose own life had been celebrated in an earlier series), but abandoned after her exile from France in 1631.

BROUWER: *A Boor Asleep* (P211)

In this unpretentious panel can be seen the paradox of Dutch and Flemish genre painting: low-life subjects painted in a wonderfully delicate manner. In the eighteenth century such subject matter deterred many English collectors, while the fine handling appealed to their French counterparts. The 3rd Marquess, who bought P211, and

Ascribed to Rembrandt *Landscape with a Coach* (P229)

the 4th Marquess shared this French taste, as can be seen by the number of fine Dutch cabinet pictures in the Collection. Brouwer lived in Haarlem and later Antwerp; both Rubens and Rembrandt owned several of his pictures, and his peasant scenes clearly influenced TENIERS, and A. and I. VAN OSTADE, all represented in this Gallery.

Ascribed to REMBRANDT: *Landscape with a Coach* (P229)

This marvellous panorama seems to encompass the whole range of human experience: rich man and poor, castle and farm, city and landscape, fair skies and foul – all achieved with an almost monochrome palette. The attribution of this picture, one of the 3rd Marquess's most impressive acquisitions, has been much debated; it shares some characteristics of landscapes from the late 1630s by both Rembrandt and his pupil Flinck. Other pictures once thought to be by Rembrandt, but now regarded as probably by his pupils are: *Rembrandt in a black cap* (P52); *The Good Samaritan* (P203); and *A Boy in fanciful costume* (P201) – all dating from the 1630s.

Metsu *The Sleeping Sportsman* (P251)

Gallery 20

(Built with Gallery 21 as a picture gallery, 1872–5)

Dutch 17th & 18th-century paintings

STEEN: *Celebrating the Birth* (P111)

At first sight the depiction of an innocent family party, this picture, as with the other works by Steen in this room, is a satire on the foolishness of man. The real father (perhaps a self-portrait) makes a cuckold's sign over the baby's head, while the official father pays the midwife; a pregnant woman sits drinking on the left. A sterile marriage may be symbolized by the broken eggs, closed jug and bed warmer (providing the only warmth in the marriage bed); and the hanging sausage – like the cuckold gesture, painted out in the nineteenth century – provides further innuendo.

METSU: *The Sleeping Sportsman* (P251)

Metsu, like Steen, was from Leiden, and shared his taste for good-humoured moralising. In P251 we are invited to laugh at the drunken sportsman, whose intemperance has

65

lost him the cockerel – and perhaps the favours of the lady ('to bird' in Dutch slang means to copulate). Other paintings by Metsu in this room, all of high quality, may be compared with works of a similar character by TER BORCH, NETSCHER and E. VAN DER NEER. In the later seventeenth century, Leiden was famous for its school of 'fine painters', in which the emphasis was on meticulous technique; the paintings of W. VAN MIERIS continued this tradition into the eighteenth century.

DE HOOCH: *A Woman peeling Apples* (P23)

Born in Rotterdam, de Hooch moved to Delft in the early 1650s and, under the influence of Maes and Vermeer, began painting quiet but exquisitely composed domestic scenes in which light is painted with great subtlety. In P23, once attributed to Vermeer, the subject is probably symbolic of domestic virtue.

De Hooch *A Woman peeling Apples* (P23)

W. VAN DE VELDE the younger:
Calm: Fishing Boats at low water (P143)

Willem the younger shared a studio with his father, Willem, and brother, ADRIAEN (whose *Noonday Rest* (P199) hangs in this Gallery). He specialized in marine subjects and, after moving to London with his father in 1672/3, he established the standard for successive generations of English marine artists. P143, dated *c.*1660, is a particularly well-balanced and delicately coloured composition. Several other fine pictures by him hang nearby, while his large and impressive *Calm: Dutch Ships coming to anchor* (P137) is in Gallery 22.

Gallery 21
Dutch 17th-century paintings influenced by the landscape and art of Italy

This Gallery is also used for temporary special exhibitions.

J. BOTH: *Italian Landscape* (P28)

Both, who came from Utrecht, was one of the first of his generation of Dutch artists to visit Italy, staying in Rome 1638–42. His paintings and those of earlier Dutch 'Italianate' artists influenced several contemporaries, including BERCHEM, A. CUYP, and PYNACKER. This picture, with its carefully structured composition and glowing colour, is typical of Both's work from the mid-1640s.

A. CUYP: *The Ferry Boat* (P54)

The Ferry Boat, like its companions by Cuyp, *Shipping on the Maas* (P49), and *The Avenue at Meerdervoort* (P51), can be dated to the early 1650s, and is perhaps the finest of the group. All three depict scenes on or near the River Maas beside Cuyp's home town of Dordrecht. Cuyp's paintings exerted a particular fascination for British collectors, and even today there are more of his works in this country than in any other.

PHILIPS WOUWERMANS: *The Horse Fair* (P65)

In the eighteenth century *The Horse Fair* was celebrated as one of Wouwermans' masterpieces and was engraved when in a French collection. Wouwermans' animated scenes then influenced Watteau and his pupils (see, for example, Lancret's *Fête in a Wood*, P448, in Gallery 24). The silvery tone of P65, from the 1660s, is even more

Wouwermans *The Horse Fair* (P65)

evident in the slightly earlier *Stream in hilly Country* (P218). *Shoeing a Horse* (P144), of *c*.1650, best displays the earlier influence on him of the Dutch Italianate painters.

BERCHEM: *The Musical Shepherdess* (P640)

Berchem, who was born in Haarlem, probably went to Italy in 1653, although he may have travelled there in 1642–5 with J. B. WEENIX, whose work certainly influenced *A Southern Harbour Scene* (P25). In P640, of 1658, both landscape and figures are painted in an idealized manner, in contrast to the naturalism of Ruisdael, Hobbema or Wijnants. Such Italianate pictures were greatly admired in the eighteenth century, but came to be disparaged (as contrived and unpatriotic) in the later nineteenth century.

Unknown Artist: *The Rape of Europa*, after Titian (P5)

Titian's original picture (now in the Isabella Stewart Gardner Museum, Boston, Mass.) is one of six scenes from Ovid's *Metamorphoses* painted for Philip II of Spain. This small copy of good quality, probably painted in the eighteenth century, is placed here so that the visitor may compare it with Titian's *Perseus and Andromeda* in Gallery 22, one of the original series.

Titian *Perseus and Andromeda* (P11)

Gallery 22
(Built as a gallery in 1872–5)

Titian, 17th-century paintings, English portraits and bronze statuettes

The largest room in Hertford House, Gallery 22 offers one of the finest displays of European painting to be seen anywhere in the world. The seventeenth century is superbly represented by pictures acquired in almost every case, including all those discussed below, by the 4th Marquess of Hertford.

TITIAN: *Perseus and Andromeda* (P I I)

Painted for Philip II of Spain in 1554 and later owned by van Dyck, for twenty years *Perseus and Andromeda* hung unrecognised over Sir Richard Wallace's bath at Hertford House (when it was thought to be by Domenichino). It is, in fact, one of Titian's most important works, painted for his greatest patron, and one of a set of six *poesie* (poetical subjects) drawn from the Roman poet Ovid (for another, see Gallery 21). It shows Andromeda chained to a rock in sacrifice to a sea monster sent by Neptune, the sea god; her mother had alleged she was more beautiful than Neptune's sea nymphs. Perseus, who chanced upon the scene, plunges down from the sky to slay the monster, watched by Andromeda's parents on the shore. Titian's placing of Andromeda as a full-length nude at one side of the picture, counterbalanced by the smaller but dramatic figure of Perseus, gorgeously clothed, is the kind of mannerist device more usually associated with his compatriot Tintoretto.

CHAMPAIGNE: *The Annunciation* (P I 34)

The archangel Gabriel tells Mary she will bear a son, Jesus, by the Holy Spirit. The splendour of the figures and their magnificent draperies are emphasized by the bareness of the interior while the remarkable simplicity of the imposing composition may reflect the influence of the Jansenist movement, an austere Catholic sect based at Port-Royal, with which Champaigne was allied. It is uncertain for which French church Champaigne painted this altarpiece, but it had been removed before 1815 when it belonged to Napoleon's uncle, Cardinal Fesch. Champaigne is magnificently represented in Gallery 22. Together with *The Annunciation*, painted probably in the 1640s, can be seen *The Adoration of the Shepherds* (P I 29), from the same period but very different in its indebtedness to Rubens, *The Marriage of the Virgin* (P I 19), which may include the artist's self-portrait on the extreme left, and the sympathetic characterisation of *An Echevin of Paris* (P I 27), a fragment cut from a group portrait of officials of the Paris City Council.

ROSA: *River Landscape with Apollo and the Cumaean Sibyl* (P116)

The subject is derived from Ovid's *Metamorphoses*. In return for her favours, Apollo offered a prophetess, the Cumaean Sibyl, anything she desired. When she asked for as many years of life as the grains of sand she held in her hands (the scene in Rosa's painting) her wish was granted. But she rebuffed Apollo, and in revenge the god did not give her perpetual youth, so she lived for centuries as a wretched hag. The picture probably dates from the 1650s and was once owned by Cardinal Mazarin. One of Rosa's largest and grandest works, the eerie landscape echoes the tragedy of the story. Rosa was a contemporary of Claude and Gaspard Dughet (see Claude's *Landscape with Apollo and Mercury* (P114) and Dughet's *Falls of Tivoli* (P139) also in Gallery 22), but, unlike them, he drew his inspiration from Italy's mountainous regions or, as here, the rugged coast near Naples, rather than the tranquil views and picturesque sites of the Roman Campagna. The 4th Marquess's purchase of this sombre and monumental work is an instance where he was not ruled by his taste for 'pleasing' pictures.

POUSSIN: *A Dance to the Music of Time* (P108)

This grave subject, an allegory typical of its time, was commissioned from Poussin by a learned patron of the fine arts in Rome, Cardinal Giulio Rospigliosi, later Pope Clement IX. The dancing group represents the perpetual cycle of the human condition: from Poverty (the male figure with the wreath of leaves), Labour leads to Riches and thus Pleasure which, indulged to excess, reverts to Poverty. The bubbles and hourglass symbolize the brevity of life, while the figure of Apollo in the sky and the term with the two-headed Janus (an old head looking back and a young head looking forward) refer to the passage of time through the day and through the ages. The picture probably dates from the late 1630s and is one of the most serious ever bought by the 4th Marquess of Hertford.

Rembrandt *Titus, the Artist's Son* (P29)

Rubens *The Rainbow Landscape* (P63) detail

REMBRANDT: *Titus, the Artist's son* (P29)

Titus van Rijn (1641–68), the only child of Rembrandt and his wife Saskia to survive infancy, is shown here at the age of about sixteen, *c.*1657. At this time he helped administer the estate of his father who had been declared bankrupt in 1656. There is a remarkable tenderness in the way Rembrandt looks at his son which is in complete contrast to the formality of the earlier Rembrandt studio portraits commissioned by the Pellicornes (P82 and P90), a rising merchant family, proud of their success.

RUBENS: *The Rainbow Landscape* (P63)

The Rainbow Landscape was painted by Rubens at the end of his life after he had retired to the château of Het Steen, between Brussels and Antwerp, in 1635. The château itself is the subject of the companion landscape in the National Gallery, London. Together, the pictures offer a glorious celebration of life. Painted for the artist's own pleasure, the pictures show contrasting aspects of a summer's day, a morning scene in the National Gallery painting and late afternoon in *The Rainbow Landscape*. A poignant analogy with the Last Judgement is suggested by the rainbow, perhaps a foreboding of the artist's approaching death.

Velázquez *The Lady with a Fan* (p88)

VAN DYCK: *Philippe Le Roy* and *Marie de Raet*
(P94 and P79)

These portraits of Philippe Le Roy (c.1596–1679), an important official in the Habsburg government of the Spanish Netherlands, and his wife, Marie de Raet (1614–42), are characteristic of the elegant style of aristocratic portraiture perfected by van Dyck. Both pictures emphasize the status of the sitters, but the confidence of the man's pose, reinforced by the tense but obedient boar hound at his side, is in marked contrast to the diffidence of his young wife and her little spaniel in the companion picture. The portrait of Le Roy is dated 1630, that of his wife 1631.

VELÁZQUEZ: *The Lady with a Fan* (P88)

At the age of twenty-four Velázquez became painter to Philip IV of Spain, and for the rest of his life he remained attached to the Spanish court, painting many members of the royal family and sitters from the court circle. Portraits of Prince Baltasar Carlos, son of Philip IV, by Velázquez and his studio can also be seen in Gallery 22 (P6 and P12). The identity of the lady in this wonderfully calm and closely observed portrait is unknown, although from her dress we may infer that she was not one of the court circle. The picture was painted c.1640.

HALS: *The Laughing Cavalier* (P84)

One of the most famous portraits in the world, yet the identity of the man is unknown. From the inscription in the upper right corner we know only that he was twenty-six years old when Hals painted him in 1624, presumably as a commission from the sitter himself. The title, inaccurate but now inseparable from the work, dates from the 1870s when it was first exhibited by Sir Richard Wallace. It had been bought by the 4th Marquess in 1865 for a record sum, but had been little noticed before this date. Its reputation is founded partly on the incomparable skill with which Hals has painted the brilliant costume (including the love emblems on the doublet), but above all on the vivid portrayal of swaggering self-confidence.

Hals *The Laughing Cavalier* (p84)

GAINSBOROUGH: *Mrs Mary Robinson ('Perdita')* (P42)

Mrs Robinson (1758–1800), an actress best known for her role as the shepherdess Perdita in *The Winter's Tale*, was the first mistress of the Prince of Wales, later George IV. Painted for the Prince in 1781, this portrait shows her holding a miniature of him in her right hand. Later she became a friend of the 2nd Marquess and Marchioness of Hertford. In an exquisitely tactless gesture, the portrait

Reynolds *Miss Nelly O'Brien* (P38)

was given to the 2nd Marquess by the Prince in 1818, just as his liaison with the 2nd Marchioness was ending, and her place was being taken by Lady Conyngham. Portraits of Mrs Robinson by Reynolds and Romney can also be seen in Gallery 22.

LAWRENCE: *George IV* (P559)

Painted for the King's mistress, Lady Conyngham, in 1822, Lawrence's image of George IV (reigned 1820–30) is remarkably informal for a full-length royal portrait of the period. Seated on a sofa by an open window, the King has next to him a Boulle table and an ormolu inkstand, French-style furniture of the kind so admired and collected both by him and the 3rd Marquess of Hertford. The picture was therefore an appropriate acquisition for the Collection when bought by Sir Richard Wallace in 1883.

REYNOLDS: *Miss Nelly O'Brien* (P38)

During the period when this portrait was painted, 1762–4, Nelly O'Brien (died 1768) became the mistress of the 3rd Viscount Bolingbroke. It is not known whether the picture was commissioned by him. The most sympathetic of several portraits by Reynolds of this sitter, who was a well-known courtesan, it is also one of his most accomplished works, particularly in the subtle handling of the dress and the shadowed face. It was bought by the 2nd Marquess of Hertford in 1810.

Gallery 23
(Built as a gallery in 1872–5)

19th-century French paintings and miniatures

(paintings are hung close together in an approximation of the manner favoured in that century)

DELACROIX: *The Execution of the Doge Marino Faliero* (P282)

Like most nineteenth-century paintings this picture was painted for sale at an exhibition rather than for a patron. Dating from 1825–26, when Delacroix was sharing a studio with Bonington and was greatly influenced by English art and literature, the subject is taken from Byron's tragedy, *Marino Faliero*. Faliero was a Doge of Venice who,

Delacroix *The Execution of the Doge Marino Faliero* (P282)

after conspiring against the state, was executed in 1355. Delacroix's figures, however, wear sixteenth-century costumes taken from paintings of the period. The romantic drama and vigour of the work set it apart from other nineteenth-century pictures in the Collection, and there is some doubt whether it was acquired by the 4th Marquess, with whose customary taste it does not agree, or by Sir Richard Wallace.

SCHEFFER: *Francesca da Rimini* (P316)

One of the most popular French paintings of the century (George Eliot said that she 'could look at it for hours'), *Francesca da Rimini* cost the 4th Marquess of Hertford more than any other of his nineteenth-century pictures. He bought it at auction in 1870, but it had originally been exhibited at the Salon of 1835. The subject, derived from Dante's *Inferno*, shows Dante, guided by Virgil, watching Paolo and Francesca in the second circle of Hell with the souls of the lustful. The lovers had been stabbed to death by Francesca's husband, who was also Paolo's elder brother. The ornate frame, which includes part of Dante's text, elaborates the story.

VERNET: *The Dog of the Regiment Wounded* (P607)

The 4th Marquess of Hertford was an enthusiastic collector of works of art and books relating to Napoleon's military exploits, due, presumably, to his upbringing in Paris during the Empire and his later friendship with Napoleon III. Horace Vernet was also a devotee of the Napoleonic legend, painting portraits of the Emperor, episodes from his life and scenes from the lives of his soldiers on and off the battlefield. Painted in 1819, *The Dog of the Regiment Wounded*, together with its pendant *The Wounded Trumpeter* (P613), were immensely popular pictures, as one might expect from their combination of sentimentality with military glamour. In 1863 the critic Sainte-Beuve remembered engravings of them 'in every shop window'.

ROQUEPLAN: *The Lion in Love* (P285)

The subject is taken from La Fontaine's *Fables*. A noble lion fell in love with a shepherdess who, like Delilah with Samson, bewitched him and removed his claws and teeth, whereupon her father set the dogs on him. The picture was a notable success at the 1836 Salon and was bought by the 4th Marquess of Hertford in 1853. Scenes from history and literature were a staple part of nineteenth-century painting, particularly for those of Lord Hertford's generation whose formative years had coincided with the full flood of romanticism in the 1820s. Within that movement, however, his taste tended towards sentimentality rather than passionate intensity.

MEISSONIER: *An Artist showing his Work* (P325)

The vogue among painters like Roqueplan, Isabey and Meissonier for subject matter derived from the eighteenth century was part of a general revival of interest in the *ancien régime* which with painting had begun by the 1840s. The revival entirely agreed with the tastes of the 4th Marquess of Hertford. Meissonier's figures in this picture (which was exhibited in the 1850–1 Salon) wear Louis XV costumes but he has shown his own pictures on the studio walls. Meissonier was perhaps the richest French painter of the nineteenth century and received the highest official honours. The 4th Marquess particularly liked his anecdotal, highly finished works and they knew each other well.

In the centre of the Gallery are two upright covered cases containing early nineteenth-century miniatures (please lift the covers). Case 1 contains miniatures of the Napoleonic period, including fine examples by Isabey and Augustin, who dominated French miniature painting in the early years of the nineteenth century. Case 2 is devoted principally to Napoleonic subjects, including portraits of the Emperor and his family.

ISABEY: *Self-portrait* (M226) (case 1)

Isabey and his studio produced hundreds of miniatures, particularly of Napoleon and his court. After 1815 he worked with equal facility for the victorious allied powers (note the *Portrait of Wellington* (M223)) and for the Bourbon monarchy. His considerable abilities can perhaps best be seen in his early work such as this *Self-portrait*, painted on ivory *c.*1800–05.

Isabey *Self-portrait*
(M226)

Gallery 24

(Formerly the dressing-rooms of Sir Richard and Lady Wallace and Lady Wallace's bathroom)

French 18th-century furniture and paintings, also miniatures

GAUDREAUS: *Chest of Drawers* (F86)

This piece of furniture is of the highest importance. It was made in 1739 for the bedchamber of Louis XV at Versailles and originally stood under a mirror which still survives in the panelling of the walls of the room. Based on a drawing by one of the Slodtz brothers, it was made by Gaudreaus with mounts by J. Caffiéri (the maker of the great chandeliers in Galleries 4 and 16). Because of the importance of the commission, Caffiéri stamped his mark on a mount along the bottom of the right-hand side. With its double bowed front and lavish mounts, the chest of drawers demonstrates the transition which took place in French furniture in the 1720s and 1730s away from the monumental style associated with A.-C. Boulle (see Gallery 2) towards more graceful and flowing forms. The marquetry is in kingwood and *satiné*.

Gaudreaus Chest of Drawers (F86)

Attributed to GAUDREAUS: *Chest of Drawers* (F85)

Once thought to be by Cressent, this chest of drawers is now attributed to Gaudreaus by analogy with a chest of drawers delivered by Gaudreaus in 1744 to Louis XV's château at Choisy. F85 was probably made for M. de Selle, a wealthy holder of a sinecure in the naval department. Made c.1740–45 and therefore slightly later than F86, it is particularly notable for its superb dragon mounts and *espagnolette* head. The marquetry is of kingwood in an oyster-work pattern, and the marble top is original.

OEBEN: Combined Toilet- and Writing-table (F110)

From the mid-eighteenth century pieces of furniture combining two or more functions were frequently produced. The workshop of Oeben in which this table was made, perhaps by Leleu (the piece carries an incised mark with his name), was noted for its production of elaborate fittings and complicated locking devices, as shown by the great roll-top desk in Gallery 15. This ingeniously designed table contains four drawers, a stamped leather writing surface and a toilet mirror. The fittings are controlled by a complex lock which allows them to be opened out in accordance with the intended use of the table.

RIESENER: *Drop-front Secretaire* (F300)

This is perhaps the most imposing of the four splendid drop-front desks (or secretaires) displayed in Gallery 24. It was made in 1780 by Riesener, the leading cabinet-maker of the period, for Marie-Antoinette's apartments at Versailles and was used by the Queen herself. The interior contains pigeon-holes and drawers for papers and writing materials. Indeed, the secretaires differ in purpose from the chests of drawers in the Gallery in being functional pieces rather than ornamental furniture within a decorative scheme. The ornate marquetry of purple, tulip and other woods is more typical of furniture of the 1760s and is indicative of the conservatism of court taste at this time.

RIESENER: *Drop-front Secretaire* (F302)

Like F300, this secretaire was made by Riesener for Marie-Antoinette, although for the Petit Trianon at Versailles rather than her apartments in the palace. The smaller size of the rooms at the Petit Trianon probably accounts for its narrow width. Delivered in 1783, it is in a more advanced

Riesener
Drop-front Secretaire
(F302)

taste than F300, particularly in its use of finely chased, naturalistic mounts. The lozenge-shaped marquetry (in *satiné* and holly) with a motif of water-lilies (in boxwood) is a feature of Riesener's work. The similar **secretaire** in Gallery 24 (F303) veneered with thuya-wood bordered with purple-wood, was also made by Riesener for Marie-Antoinette at Versailles and is displayed with a **corner cupboard** (F275) made *en suite*.

WATTEAU: *The Music Party* (P410)

The 4th Marquess of Hertford was an enthusiastic admirer of the pictures of Watteau and his pupils Lancret and Pater. Their elegance had a particular appeal for the rich collectors of the Second Empire after a period of comparative neglect during and after the Revolution. *The Music Party*, painted *c.*1718, is the most elaborate of several pictures with the theme of a standing musician playing before a small group of elegantly dressed listeners. The mood of dalliance among the figures, hinted rather than expressed, is a characteristic feature of Watteau's subtle scenes, as is the ambiguous stage-like setting.

WATTEAU: *Gilles and his Family* (P381)

The theatre had a great influence on Watteau's subject matter as well as the structure of his compositions. The figures in *Gilles and his Family* and in *Harlequin and Columbine* (P387) wear the costume of characters in the Italian *commedia dell'arte*, although we know from a drawing that the model for the guitarist dressed as Gilles is Watteau's friend Pierre Sirois, a dealer in glass. It is perhaps in paintings on a small scale like this that Watteau came closest to the matchless delicacy of his drawings.

FRAGONARD: *The Swing* (P430)

Before painting this picture in 1767, Fragonard was thought to be destined for a great career as a history painter, the most esteemed calling for an eighteenth-century artist. But after receiving the commission for this work from an unknown patron, he turned increasingly to genre scenes, portraits and landscapes, usually in a high-spirited and decorative manner. The range of his art is well shown in Gallery 24, from his early *Musical Contest* (P471), very much in the style of his master Boucher, to the more sombre and sculptural *Fountain of Love* (P394) of the 1780s. The exuberance of *The Swing* has come to epitomize painting under the *ancien régime*, but with little historical accuracy. The fact that the history painters (except David) have been largely forgotten, and were to be of no interest to nineteenth-century collectors like the 4th Marquess of Hertford, would have astonished most observers of Fragonard's own generation.

Fragonard *The Swing* (P430)

Boizot, Gouthière and Delunésy The Avignon Clock (F258)

In the centre of the gallery are two covered hexagonal cases containing English and Continental miniatures from the sixteenth to the end of the eighteenth centuries (please lift the covers). Both portraits and subject paintings (mostly scenes of gallantry) are well represented.

HORENBOUT: *Portrait of Holbein* (M203)

For long thought to be a self-portrait by Holbein, the style of this miniature (case 2) is now believed to be closer to the work of Lucas Horenbout, who taught Holbein the techniques of miniature painting. Painted on vellum in 1543, the year of Holbein's death, it may well be a memorial portrait.

HALL: *The Painter's Family* (M186)

The Swedish-born Hall established himself as the leading portrait miniaturist soon after he settled in Paris in 1766. This work in case 1 was painted on ivory in the mid-1770s.

Gallery 25

(Formerly Lady Wallace's bedroom)

French 18th-century furniture and paintings

BOIZOT, GOUTHIÈRE and DELUNÉSY: The Avignon Clock (F258)

Designed by the sculptor Boizot, and cast, chased and gilt by Gouthière, this mantel clock, with a movement by Delunésy, was presented by the city of Avignon to the marquis de Rochechouart in 1771. In 1768 Rochechouart had taken back Avignon from papal control on behalf of Louis XV and had become its governor. The figure representing the city holds a wreath over the Rochechouart coat of arms, while the reclining male figure represents the River Rhône and the seated female its tributary, the Durance.

GOUTHIÈRE: Perfume Burner (F292)

The tripod of this perfume burner, with its bowl of red jasper, is one of the finest works of Gouthière, the leading maker of gilt bronzes before the Revolution. Later eighteenth-century bronzes are notably more delicate than those produced earlier in the century. The perfume burner was made in the 1770s for the duc d'Aumont (who after the death of Louis XV also owned the great chest of drawers F86 in Gallery 24) and was acquired at his sale in 1782 by Marie-Antoinette.

DUBOIS: Chest of Drawers (F245)

This chest of drawers was once thought to have been the marriage coffer of Marie-Antoinette. Made in the 1760s, it combines neo-classical and Oriental elements, a slightly eccentric combination but one frequently found in furniture of this period. The gilt-bronze caryatids are in the style of the sculptor Falconet and the oval plaque is of Japanese lacquer combined with a fretted mount of pseudo-Oriental character.

BOUCHER: *Jupiter and Callisto* (P446)

Boucher's art contains numerous erotic mythological subjects. The four rectangular canvases with scenes in which Venus plays a prominent part (P429, P432, P438 and P444) were not originally a set, but by 1851 they had been mounted together on a folding screen. The large oval *Jupiter and Callisto*, dated 1769, is one of Boucher's last works and shows the blander handling and colour of his final years. Jupiter, disguised as Diana, seduces Callisto, one of Diana's hunting nymphs.

BOUCHER: *Madame de Pompadour* (P418)

Jeanne-Antoinette Poisson (1721–64) became the mistress of Louis XV and was created marquise de Pompadour in 1745. A lavish supporter of the arts, she took a close interest both in the sumptuous furnishing of her town houses and châteaux and in the fortunes and products of the Sèvres porcelain factory. From Boucher she commissioned portraits, and mythological and religious works. Indeed, of the twelve known portraits by Boucher, seven are of Madame de Pompadour. This example, signed and dated 1759, shows her standing beside a sculpture portraying Friendship consoling Love, very close in design to a work which she had commissioned from Pigalle to symbolize her later, platonic relationship with the king.

Boucher *Madame de Pompadour* (P418)

Wallace Collection Publications

Catalogues

Pictures I   British, German, Italian, Spanish, by J.Ingamells, 1985
Pictures II   French Nineteenth Century, by J.Ingamells, 1986
Pictures III French before 1815, by J.Ingamells, 1989
Pictures IV Dutch and Flemish, by J.Ingamells, 1992
Miniatures, by G.Reynolds, 1980
Illuminated Manuscript Cuttings, by J.J.G.Alexander, 1980
Sculpture, by J.G.Mann, 1931, with Supplement 1982
Furniture, by F.J.B.Watson, 1956
Pottery, Maiolica, Faience, Stoneware, by A.V.B.Norman, 1976
Sèvres Porcelain, 3 vols., by R.J.Savill, 1988
European Arms and Armour, 2 vols., by J.G.Mann, 1962
European Arms and Armour Supplement, by A.V.B.Norman, 1986
Oriental Arms and Armour, by G.F.Laking, 1913,
with Supplement 1964

The History and Description of the Collection

Guide to the Armouries, 1982
The Founders of the Wallace Collection, by P.Hughes, 1981
The Hertford Mawson Letters, by J.Ingamells, 1981
The 3rd Marquess of Hertford as a Collector, by J.Ingamells, 1983

Monographs

Mrs Robinson and her Portraits, by J.Ingamells, 1978
Preferences in French Furniture, by G.de Bellaigue, 1979
Richard Parkes Bonington, by J.Ingamells, 1980
Eighteenth-Century France and the East, by P.Hughes, 1981
Rembrandt 1892, by J.Ingamells, 1992

Picture Books

Forty Paintings, 1977
Sèvres Porcelain, by R.J.Savill, 1981
Glass, by S.Gaynor, 1984
French Gold Boxes, by R.J.Savill, 1991

Regulations for Visitors

To safeguard the Collection and to serve the public interest, the following regulations are to be observed by all visitors in Hertford House

It is not permitted to touch the works of art, to smoke, to take photographs, to play radios/tape-recorders, or to consume refreshments.

Large bags, non-folding umbrellas and sticks (unless in a case of infirmity) must be deposited in the cloakroom where they will be kept at the owner's risk.

Any bag, parcel or receptacle brought into the building may be searched by security staff.

The doors of the House occasionally have to be closed for security reasons; visitors will then be unable to leave until the emergency is ended.

Due to the many small rooms and the dense display of objects of art, prams and push-chairs are not permitted in the House. Invalid chairs are allowed and a lift is available.

No work of art may be brought into the House without permission from security staff. No work of art may be removed from the House without a pass signed by a Curator.

A visitor requesting an interview with a member of staff, or wishing to inspect a work of art not on display, must first complete a visitor's form as directed by security staff.

Prior notification is required from all visiting parties. School parties must be satisfactorily supervised. Numbers are normally limited to twenty-five.

Groups with a guide lecturer cannot be admitted to a gallery where an official lecture is in progress.

Sketching is permitted in a dry medium. Easels, brushes, paints and water are not permitted and sharpening blades/knives must be kept concealed.

Security staff may refuse admission or instruct to leave any person whose presence appears likely to cause annoyance to other visitors or to endanger the works of art.

No person shall remain in the House after closing time without the permission of a Curator.

By order of the Trustees of the Wallace Collection

Board of Trustees

Buses
(Stopping at Selfridges)
2A, 2B, 6, 7, 8, 10, 12, 13, 15, 16A, 73, 74, 82, 88, 94, 113, 135, 137, 159

Underground
Bond Street
(*Central & Jubilee Lines*)
Marble Arch (*Central Line*)
Oxford Circus (*Central, Bakerloo & Victoria Lines*)
Baker Street
(*Bakerloo, Jubilee, Hammersmith and City, Metropolitan & Circle Lines*)

The Wallace Collection is a five-minute walk from Bond Street Underground Station and Oxford Street.

Coaches may stop outside Hertford House to drop and pick up passengers; the nearest coach park is at Bayswater Road, w8, opposite St. Petersburgh Place (NCP, telephone 071-499 7050).

There are no restaurant facilities but there are many restaurants in the area. A wheelchair is available at the front entrance for the disabled and there is a lift to the first floor. All works of art on display are shown on the ground and first floors.

Public lectures on aspects of the Collection are given on weekdays and at weekends. Tours and study days can also be arranged. Enquiries should be addressed to the Education Officer, The Wallace Collection, Hertford House, Manchester Square, London w1m 6bn.